HOW STEAM LOCOMOTIVES WORK

HOW STEAM LOCOMOTIVES WORK

DAVID WILSON

Argus Books

Argus Books
Argus House
Boundary Way
Hemel Hempstead
Herts HP2 7ST
England

First published by Argus Books 1993

Photography by Peter Herring

ISBN 1 85486 080 1

Phototypesetting and design by The Studio, Exeter.
Printed and bound in Great Britain by BPCC Wheatons Ltd, Exeter.

Contents

HOW STEAM LOCOMOTIVES WORK

Introduction

To understand how the steam locomotive works it is useful to understand something of where the locomotive came from, just what are its antecedants and possibly to have some form of explanation as to why the steam locomotive enjoyed the status and popularity it did, and still does, enjoy. In purely historical terms the steam locomotive is a young upstart — it didn't make its first public appearance until the first decade of the nineteenth century.

In 1802 a young Cornish engineer by the name of Richard Trevithick created a steam locomotive which used toothed gear wheels to move along a track. It was less than successful. In 1804 he built a second locomotive which dispensed with the geared drive and trials were conducted with this second engine at the Pen-y-Darren tramroad, in the South Wales coalfield, to ascertain whether or not a steam engine could do the work of the horse. These trials were not a great success either; much damage was caused to the lines and the adhesion of the locomotive left something to be desired.

1809 Trevithick was back, this time with the famous 'Catch Me Who Can'. The 'Catch Me Who Can' was a kind of fairground ride — a circle of track was laid out just off Euston Road in London, and people could ride round the track hauled by Trevithick's steam locomotive. These hardly seem like the beginnings of an invention which would 'change the world'.

In understanding the phenomena of the steam engine and railways it may help you to learn a little of the background in which steam traction came about. In 1804 the idea of work from steam was not new. In the last decades of the seventeenth century the Frenchman Cugnot built a steam-driven three-wheeled vehicle. Though not a railway vehicle, it was a serious attempt to make steam mobile. Steam condensing engines were in use from the last decade of the seventeenth century, and by the first decades of the eighteenth century they were in use pumping water from deep mines, driving winding wheels on rope-worked inclines and other such tasks. However, these engines were of the condensing type — very large, utilising heavy beams and parts, they were extremely inefficient and completely immobile.

In the second half of the eighteenth century the Quaker, Abraham Darby, had set up an iron foundry by the banks of the River Severn at Coalbrookedale in Shropshire, and begun to put into practice techniques learned from tinkers in the Netherlands. Trevithick collaborated with Darby's foundry in building his locomotives — the cylinder blocks were cast at Coalbrookedale, which was, arguably, one of the most important sites in the creation of the industrial revolution. The main problems which exercised the minds of Trevithick and the Coalbrookedale ironmasters were how to reduce the weight whilst retaining the strength of the locomotive, and how to increase the tensile strength of the track.

Despite their collaboration, not the least of the difficulties for Trevithick was that his locomotive continued to break the track. The first attempts at steam locomotion may have been less than impressive yet one hundred years later the steam locomotive had 'changed the world'.

Several contemporaneous events transpired to ensure that Trevithick's early tinkerings did not go to waste. The events themselves were quite diverse: one was the Napoleonic Wars; another the growth of manufacturing; yet another was a shortage of horses and horse feed; even Turnpike Laws had their effects.

Wealthy pit owners were having their profits eaten into on the one hand by the cost of horses and feed and on the other by their inability to move their goods quickly and in large enough quantities. The more farsighted amongst them encouraged their colliery engineers or overmen to investigate any possible ways around this impasse.

One such wealthy soul was Charles Brandling, owner of numerous pits in the Leeds area. Brandling instructed his colliery deputy, or overman, John Blenkinsop, to seek alternative sources of traction to that of horse or man. Blenkinsop, in conjunction with a wandering flax mill engineer called Matthew Murray and financed by Brandling, began work on a steam locomotive of which it may be said that in itself it was successful; but certain features of it were not.

The locomotive built by Murray and Blenkinsop was given the name *Salamanca* and she began her active career in 1812. During the same year, 1812, George Stephenson, who was at that time investigating the use of steam traction for his boss at Killingworth Colliery, near Newcastle-upon-Tyne, visited Brandling's railway to inspect *Salamanca*.

At this time the big debate was, would adhesion alone be sufficient to enable the locomotive to move loaded wagons and, in particular, move them up a gradient? Murray and Blenkinsop were of the belief that more than simple adhesion was required and *Salamanca* was fitted with a large toothed wheel which engaged a toothed rail laid alongside the running line — a sort of precursor to the rack railway, which did not come about until many years later. However, this rack rail feature of the Murray/Blenkinsop system was not adopted and less than a year later William Hedley's *Puffing Billy* showed that simple adhesion was sufficient to enable the locomotive to move a load against a gradient.

Stephenson's first effort at a steam locomotive, *Blucher*, entered traffic in July 1814, shortly after Hedley's *Puffing Billy* which went into service at Wylam Colliery in 1813. These were the first spindly locomotives and mechanical stirrings from

the men who became the 'midwives' to what was to be dubbed 'The Railway Age'.

The real success of Murray/Blenkinsop's effort was that steam power was successfully used to haul coals in almost unheard of quantities, reportedly one hundred tons at a brisk walking pace. Like the efforts of Murray and Blenkinsop, those of Hedley and Stephenson were also relatively successful — though by no means could they be described as completely so. The problems were caused by what we today would call a lack of technology and by the lack of a precedent. Everything was a matter of trial and error. However, these early pioneers refused to be beaten and the colliery owners continued to provide funds and facilities for their continued experimentation.

Breakdowns, shortages of steam, broken rails and failures of design all plagued the early years of steam. For some years it was touch-and-go whether the use of steam locomotion would continue. Some have argued that had Timothy Hackworth not worked on and improved upon Stephenson's designs, steam traction might well not have kept going, particularly on the all-important Stockton and Darlington Railway.

When Stephenson was given the task of building the Stockton and Darlington he took on Hackworth and appointed him locomotive superintendent of the Stockton and Darlington Railway, with his headquarters at Shildon Works. It was Hackworth's 'Royal George' design which finally showed that steam power could be successfully utilised as a more expedient means of transport than the horse and cart.

Twenty-three years had elapsed between Trevithick's first locomotive crushing the tracks at Pen-y-Darren and Hackworth's *Royal George* crushing the opposition on the original 'Slow and Dirty', the Stockton and Darlington. The next twenty-five years would see a staggering growth in the railway network, not just in Britain but throughout Europe and the Americas.

The Stockton and Darlington opened in 1825; the *Royal George* first ran on it in 1827 and by 1853 there were railways in America (1830), France (1832), Ireland (1834), Belgium and Germany (1835), Canada (1836), Cuba and Russia (1837), Italy and Czechoslovakia (1839), Poland (1842), Switzerland (1844), Jamaica (1845),

Austria-Hungary and the Balkans (1846), Denmark (1847), Spain and British Guiana (1848), Mexico (1850), Chile and Peru (1851) and the Indian sub-continent (1853).

By any standards this growth is phenomenal and when you consider that in this same period two thirds of the British railway network was built, it seems even more remarkable. That it was built with pick and shovel, dynamite and donkey work makes the achievement all the more extraordinary.

To cope with this growth in railways there was an equally prodigious growth in the mining of coals and the production of steel and iron, without which it would not have been possible to build the lines and locomotives. More than any other invention, it was the steam locomotive which provided and allowed for the expansion of the economy. It might be argued that no developed economy has ever been achieved without the railway; certainly no developed country has arrived at that position without building railway lines in the process.

For Britain all things railway became a major export earner. British companies built the locomotives for foreign railways — they supplied the workmen to build the lines, the engineers to design them and, in some cases, the capital with which to build them. The first locomotive in Russia was transported there from Britain by Hackworth's son, who even taught the Czar of Russia how to drive the locomotive.

This thumbnail sketch of the birth of the railway age doesn't explain why the railways, and the steam locomotive in particular, became so popular. For an answer to this conundrum we need to look not to history, but to the human condition. The railways were founded on the premise that they would make profits from the carriage of goods and merchandise. However, for the first twenty years of their existence the railways earned more from passenger traffic receipts than from freight charges — in other words the general public took to the railway in droves.

It is my contention that some of the reasons for the enduring popularity of the steam locomotive are to be found in philosophies that were effectively done away with by the growth of science, industry, the railways and so-called progress. One of these ancient philosophies held that things were made up of varying proportions of four elements; earth, air, fire and water. All substances contained one or more of these elements combined together in varied proportions depending on the nature of the substance.

The steam locomotive incorporates and employs all these elements in its construction and in its performance. Fire, from burning the product of the earth — coal — turns water into air — steam/water vapour, the relation to the cloud! Not only does the locomotive harmoniously combine and harness the four elements into power and motion, it utilises the same four elements in its construction. Ores of the earth are smelted in the furnace by air being forced through the fire. Water is used to temper the metals into varying types and alloys used in the locomotive's construction.

In Gaston Bachelard's *Psychoanalysis of Fire,* he puts forward the argument that man's relationship with fire has profound effects not only upon his psyche but also upon his science and that the four elements are, "...elements of imaginative experience and always will be".

It is fire which is at the very heart of the steam locomotive. It is the fire which transforms the lifeless metals and the cold damp waters into the roaring, living, breathing machine. A machine which conquers all before it: hills and mountains, rivers and streams, counties, countries and continents. The fire which creates the steam (and thus the 'steam locomotive') is started, tended and maintained by man. This is not the raging uncontrolled fire of the forest or the destroyer of house and home, but the harnessed provider, Prometheus Bound!

The steam locomotive is an extraordinary symbiosis of man and machine. It depends on the men on its footplate to be able to produce any sort of performance. In the cab of a diesel or electric locomotive, the driver operates controls which set the locomotive in motion or stop it. The performance delivered by those controls is predetermined. That is, for a given load, gradient, wind speed and direction a specific amount of diesel fuel or electrical force will be consumed, but the energy content of the electricity or the diesel fuel does not alter — you don't get a cable full of cheap electricity but you can and do get a tender full of poor grade coal.

There is no comparison between the relationship of the footplate crew to its steam locomotive and that of the crew to the diesel or electric locomotive. On the diesel or electric locomotive the goods are delivered, at least in theory, as long as the driver opens the power controller. On the steam locomotive the power is delivered only if the driver and fireman work together with the locomotive as a team.

This symbiotic relationship between the men and the machine needs to be borne in mind when considering 'how the steam locomotive works'. When it works, it does so because of the skill and ability of the footplatemen. In the following chapters we will be discussing the way in which the various parts which make up the steam locomotive come together to create the operational whole, but it should always be remembered that the overall ability and efficiency of the steam locomotive is, in many respects, determined not by the design or the designer, but by the men of the footplate.

The fascination for the steam locomotive was once considered the domain of the schoolboy and the eccentric. The 'train-spotter' with his anorak and duffle bag, clutching note-book and pencil became a stereotype. However, today the interest in the steam locomotive is spread across the whole spectrum — postmen to politicians, barristers to bricklayers — and there are growing numbers of women becoming involved in the operational aspects of running a steam-powered railway.

The restoration and preservation of the steam locomotive and the operation of over one hundred preserved steam railways the length and breadth of Britain, is now a leisure pursuit which boasts over one hundred thousand serious followers and, perhaps more importantly, these 'private railways' collectively carry over five million passengers each year. Every weekend some twenty thousand enthusiasts work as volunteers on lines which they themselves have saved from oblivion.

The steam engine, as it was most often referred to, ceased to be the motive power of our national railway network in 1968. This though was not the end, for since 1968 hundreds of steam locomotives have been saved from the cutter's torch and have been rebuilt, repaired and restored to their original condition.

Despite this degree of popularity and the antiquity of the technology, many people (and even a goodly number of the enthusiasts themselves) have only the vaguest idea as to how the steam locomotive works and what precisely are the parts from which it is constructed. The aim of this book is, hopefully, to dispel this ignorance and explain in plain English how and why the steam locomotive works. What does make it tick — or should that be puff? Each chapter will cover a specific area of the construction of the locomotive and give details of the various parts which are combined to create the area under discussion.

Steam locomotives have been designed and constructed by some highly autocratic and extremely individualistic men (and to my knowledge all the chief mechanical engineers of the steam era were men). These CMEs have their champions — men and women who will not hear a bad word said about the products of 'their' designer. The CME is the man who signs the drawings produced by the drawing office draughtsmen and is ultimately responsible for the design and subsequent performance of a particular locomotive. The names of some of these men are almost as legendary as the locomotives they designed: Sir Nigel Gresley, Sir William A. Stanier F.R.S., Daniel Gooch, H. A. Ivatt, Patrick Stirling, G. J. Churchward, Oliver Bulleid and many more.

Intense commercial rivalries existed between the railway companies and they fought long and hard to attract more business to their routes as opposed to those of their rivals. One way in which this rivalry manifested itself was in the size, power and speed of their respective locomotive fleets.

In the 1880s and 1890s there were the famous 'railway races to the north' in which numerous companies competed in running trains over the two routes to Aberdeen — one via Crewe and Carlisle, the west coast route; the other via Doncaster and Newcastle, the east coast route. Similar competition existed between the London and South Western Railway and the Great Western over the traffic from Plymouth to London.

This rivalry and competition was a spur to the design and development of the steam locomotive but this was not the only way that developments in steam locomotive technology were brought about. Almost from the very beginnings of the railway age there were accidents and disasters and these too had their influence upon locomotive design and development. Sometimes the improvements and modifications came about as the result of actions taken by the companies themselves, but all too often the improvements were forced on the companies by Parliament, because they had failed to take the necessary remedial actions.

The development of the steam locomotive has been well charted in a vast array of texts and so I will take many of the developmental aspects as read. However, there are some which will be incorporated into this work — items such as the use of 'superheating', the development and use of the 'continuous vacuum brake' and improvements brought about by the advance of parallel technologies such as improved welding techniques or more highly specialised steels and lubricants.

These developmental aspects will be covered in the relevant chapters rather than being set into a chapter of their own. Thus the chapter covering the smokebox will also cover the development of the various types of blastpipe. Similarly the chapter concerned with the firebox will cover improvements in welding and X-ray techniques which led to the welded firebox.

In addition to a description of the parts and how they fit together, an attempt will be made to explain how the parts under discussion are incorporated into the whole, and then how that whole operates. An example might be to say that a 'stay' is a piece of threaded metal, which may be made of steel or copper; that they are used in the construction of the firebox and are also used to join the firebox to the boiler barrel. Following from this description may be a further explanation as to the need for the stay and why it is necessary to use this method to join together the inner and outer sheets of steel or copper which comprise the firebox.

By the very nature of the subject material, the incorporation of technical terms and jargon within the text is inevitable, but wherever they are used a simple explanation, or an analogy, will be provided. Hopefully, this will allow those with only the most basic understanding of the steam locomotive to understand the descriptions of its workings and build up a knowledge of its construction and the parts used in that construction.

I have chosen to begin the description of the workings and construction of the steam locomotive with the firebox. The choice of any particular starting point is fairly arbitrary, but the firebox has been selected because this is the area where the generating of the motive power, steam, begins. In addition to the chapters covering the parts of the locomotive and their operational activities I have also included a chapter dealing with the various tests which the locomotive must undergo before being pronounced as fit for active service. For their help in preparing this, I am grateful to British Rail's chief steam locomotive examiners, Sam Foster and Brian Penney.

In any work covering such a huge subject area there are inevitably omissions of one sort or another, though I hope that in this book these are minimal and do not leave unanswered questions. In particular the omissions are what might best be described as idiosyncrasies. However, one or two of the more noteworthy experimental locomotive types are included as historic footnotes. These include such locomotives as the Stanier Pacific No 6202 — (the Turbomotive) the Royal Scot class locomotive No 6170 *Fury,* which was fitted with the high pressure boiler, the use of 'boosters' or powered bogie wheels, feed water heating, condensing apparatus and articulated locomotives such as the Garratts and Fairlies. However, complete eccentricities such as the highly dubious water bottom ashpan of Webb will be deemed beyond the scope of this work which is, after all, intended as a layman's guide to the steam locomotive and how it works.

Many, if not all, books are dedicated to someone and in keeping with that tradition I would like to dedicate this work to the steam locomotive enginemen — the men who brought the steam locomotive to life!

CHAPTER 1

The Hearth of the Matter

Like all good stories and as with every serious explanation we need to begin at the beginning and so we shall. In order to make a steam engine work you need steam and to be able to raise steam you must have two ingredients — heat and water — and the means to apply the former to the latter. In the steam locomotive the process which creates steam takes place in the area referred to as the firebox.

In simple terms the firebox is just that — a large box filled with flaming coals and surrounded by a water jacket. Heat from the burning coals is transmitted through the metal and thus heats the water trapped in the water jacket. In turn the water prevents the burning coals from heating the metal to the point where it would melt — just like a kettle. As long as the kettle is full of water no problem, but let the water boil away and — whoops! — the bottom of the kettle melts.

In crude terms the foregoing is what is happening in the locomotive firebox, but a more thorough explanation is needed. The firebox is one part of the construction of the locomotive's boiler (the other sections of this construction will be dealt with in subsequent chapters). Generally speaking the firebox is at one end of the boiler

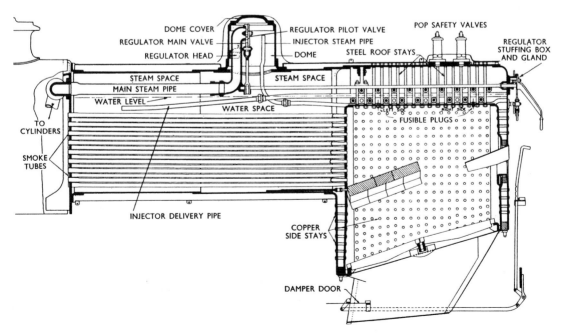

Cross section through a typical boiler, indicating the staying of the firebox, the baffle plate and the brick arch. Note the steam space at the top of the boiler and the dome, containing the main steam pipe to the cylinders.

barrel and the smokebox at the other. However, this has not always been the case. Some of the earliest locomotives had a firebox and smokebox at the same end of the boiler barrel — the design was referred to as the return flue boiler.

In practice this meant that much of the heat from the fire went straight out of the chimney instead of being imparted to the water. The first locomotive to use the multi-flue/tube boiler to gain maximum heat from the burning fuel was *Rocket* — which like all early locomotives burned coke, not coal. However, *Rocket* did contain in its construction all the elements of the 'modern' steam locomotive: exhaust from the cylinders was fed into the base of the chimney, in turn creating a vacuum in the smokebox and hence a

draught on the fire. And, of course, the afore-mentioned multi-tubed boiler is another of the hallmarks of the 'modern' steam locomotive.

Today, over one hundred and fifty years after *Rocket* was constructed, the only alterations to the steam locomotive boiler have been minimal tinkerings rather than any radical departure from the basic concepts embodied in *Rocket*. The changes have been items such as the move to superheating in 1906, the use of welded fireboxes and thermic siphons in the 1940s, the use of multi-jet blastpipes from the 1930s and, of course, the great increases in size.

The firebox in the single flue engine and in multi-flue locomotives like *Rocket* and its modern equivalents, is at the opposite end of the boiler

The Swindon precept of Belpaire firebox, taper boiler and top feed to the boiler was laid down by George Jackson Churchward and perpetuated throughout subsequent designs by Charles Collett and Frederick Hawksworth. The Belpaire firebox, whose rectangular construction increased the water space, is well illustrated in this close-up of Castle Class 7P 4-6-0 No 5029 *Nunney Castle*.

from the chimney. In the single return flue type the firebox is at the same end of the boiler as the chimney. Today we think of the engine with the firebox alongside the chimney as antiquated but in their day they were at the forefront.

In modern locomotive practice there are several major types or designs of firebox but the basic principles apply to all of them. There is a grate upon which the coals are burned (when I use the term coals I am referring to the combustible material, which could also be wood, coke or oil). There is an opening through which additional coals may be added, a means to admit air to the fire and a water jacket of some sort to prevent the fire from melting the metal.

British locomotives have been based around three types of firebox: round topped, wide and Belpaire. The round topped firebox is most generally associated with locomotives of the former London and North Eastern Railway and with most, though not quite all, locomotive designs prior to 1891. The Belpaire firebox, named after its Belgian originator, was introduced into British locomotive practice in 1891 on the then Manchester, Sheffield and Lincoln Railway,

subsequently the backbone of the Great Central Railway. From this date the use of the Belpaire firebox became widespread, becoming more or less the norm on the GWR and LMS, under Stanier, except for his Pacific designs.

The Belpaire firebox is essentially a flat-topped firebox, an arrangement which offers the maximum steam and water space and the most convenient arrangement of stays. The third type of firebox, the wide type may be of either flat- or round-topped construction.

The difference between the wide type firebox (which is most commonly used in post-grouping Pacific designs and in some pre-grouping Atlantics) and the others is that the wide type sits across the frames whilst the others sit between them. Often locomotives with a wide firebox have a set of trailing wheels mounted on some form of bogie arrangement to support the firebox as well as improving the riding of the locomotive. Exceptions to this use of a trailing wheel support are the 9F 2-10-0 heavy freight design of R. A. Riddles for British Railways and those he also designed for the Ministry of Supply during the Second World War. (In British

That most famous of steam locomotives, Gresley LNER A3 Pacific No 4472 *Flying Scotsman*, illustrates the 'wide' type of firebox which was employed on both the LNER and LMS Pacifics (and subsequent BR Standard designs). As is evident here, the 'wide' firebox stretched over the locomotive frames rather than being sited between them.

Lower half of the wide firebox and ashpan employed on the Standard Class 9F freight locomotive. Primary air to the firebed is drawn through the ashpan and controlled by the dampers.

locomotive practice one comes to learn that there are always exceptions and as we progress through this book we will come across many more.)

There have, inevitably, been one or two variations on the firebox/boiler theme. A vertical boiler was incorporated in some designs, mostly shunting and narrow-gauge types, and there have been experiments with high pressure marine-type boilers, such as that used in the experimental high pressure development of a Royal Scot class engine No 6170 *Fury* and the Gresley 'water tube' 4-6-4 No 10000. Both locomotives were later rebuilt to orthodox working.

Water-tube fireboxes were used on some early locomotives (i.e. in addition to the water jacket around the firebox there were water-filled tubes in the upper part of the firebox). However, the three main types plus the vertical variant are the only types which were used in significant numbers in British locomotive practice during the twentieth century.

The firebox is actually two boxes, an inner box usually made of copper and an outer box made of steel (in early locomotive practice wrought iron was used in place of steel). Between these two boxes is the water and steam space. The inner and outer fireboxes are tied together by 'stays'. The stays themselves can be of steel or copper construction and they come in a variety of types and sizes depending on their position within the firebox construction as a whole.

The most numerous of the stays are the 'side stays', these are also the ones most likely to be made of copper. As their name implies these stays are located in the sides and front and back plates of the firebox. However, they are not the only stays in the front and rear plates of the firebox; here they are joined by the 'palm stay', and the 'longitudinal stay'.

The palm stays are relatively few in number and they are located on the lower front part of the firebox where it is joined to the boiler barrel. The longitudinal stays, which like the palm stays are few in number, run from the firebox back-plate to the front or smokebox tubeplate and, like the palm stays, they help in securing the firebox to the boiler, though it should be noted that the firebox is also rivetted to the first ring of the boiler barrel. Almost everything concerned with the construction of the boiler is 'belt and braces'.

In the roof or 'crown' of the firebox are the crown stays and the fusible plugs. The crown stays are most usually made of steel and unlike the side stays, which are rivetted over, the crown stays are secured by large nuts.

The main safety devices associated with the firebox are the fusible plugs which are designed to prevent serious damage to the firebox in the event of the boiler becoming very low on water. The fusible plug is essentially a large bolt with a lead core which is screwed into the firebox crown plate with the tip of the plug protruding into the water/steam space above the firebox crown. If the water level falls below the tip of the plug the lead core melts and thus allows steam to escape into the firebox, damping the fire as it does so and indicating to the footplate crew that water must be put into the boiler immediately.

The lower part of the firebox consists of the grate and the foundation ring. The foundation ring is sandwiched between the inner and outer firebox plates while the grate is the area bounded by the inner firebox plates. The grate can have several different forms of construction: the rocking grate, the drop grate and the plain barred grate.

All three types of grate are of barred construction. The differences are that the rocking grate utilises small bars mounted on shafts, which in turn are connected via levers to a point on the footplate from where they can be tipped or rocked back and forth thus allowing the fire to drop between them. This makes the cleaning of the fire at the end of each turn of duty much easier for the crew.

The drop grate is similar to the rocking grate in that it is lever operated, but instead of the whole grate area being movable only a portion of it is. This movable portion can be tipped through approximately ninety degrees and the dirty fire and clinker can then be pushed down the hole which is created by the opening of the grate.

The simple bar grate was the most common form, though from about the end of the First World War the drop grate and then the rocking grate became more widespread. The rocking grate was standard on locomotives built to BR design after nationalisation.

The only other real difference in the firegrate was whether it was of level or sloping construction. As a general rule of thumb a small engine would have a flat grate and larger locomotives would have a grate in which the first row of bars would be flat and the second and third rows would slope slightly toward the firebox tubeplate. The length of the firebar varies from around two to four feet and the number of rows of bars in any firebox depends on the size of the box/bar combination — two, three or four rows were the norm. The wide type grate was, in general, of level construction and many of the locomotives fitted with this type of grate were also fitted with either the rocking or drop grate assembly.

Inside the firebox is the 'brick arch' which is generally made of pre-formed fire brick, though in modern-day preservation circles concrete is sometimes used as a substitute. The arch, which is butted up to both sides of the firebox, slopes upward and outward from the firebox tubeplate from a point just below the lowest row of tubes.

The brick arch fulfils a number of roles. One is to ensure that as much as possible of the combustible gas is turned into heat — it does this by making the volatile gases given off by the burning coal pass over the firebed before being drawn through the tubes. It also helps to prevent small pieces of coal and char being drawn onto the tubeplate or through the tubes into the smokebox; another function is to help in reducing heating and cooling stress on the firebox.

A major source of damage to the fire side of the firebox plates is that caused by small coals and char flying about in the firebox during the combustion process. The brick arch doesn't eliminate this but it does help protect the vulnerable tube ends and the tubeplate.

The type of fire brick used in the construction of the brick arch retains heat. It is this retained heat which helps reduce stress in the metal by moderating the cooling process when the fire is removed or only a small portion is kept alight, as is the case when the locomotive is between duties or when being taken out of service for repair or maintenance.

Likewise the brick arch helps to reduce stress in the firebox when the locomotive is on duties which alternate between periods of intense activity followed by periods of inaction. Examples of such duties might be freight trains which are turned in and out of passing loops to allow faster services to pass, or suburban services where quick dashes between one station and the next are followed by lengthy periods of station time.

Below the firegrate are the ashpans (or ash hoppers in the case of locomotives fitted with drop or rocking grates), which, in addition to being the collecting point of particles of burnt coals/cinders, also form an essential element in the process of combustion. In order to make a fire burn there must be air and it is through the ashpans that 'primary air' is admitted to the firebed.

The ashpans or hoppers are fitted with flaps or doors which can be controlled, either by levers or by a worm screw arrangement from the footplate. The opening and closing of these flaps — 'dampers' as they are termed — determines the volume of air passing through the firebed. In normal operation the rear damper would be open when running engine first and the front damper would be opened for tender — or bunker — first running.

The air supply to the firebed via the ashpans is referred to as primary air in order to distinguish it from air which enters the firebox through the firehole door on the footplate — 'secondary air'. There are two fittings in the firehole door, the lip plate and the baffle plate. The former sits on the lower half of the firehole and protects the firebox plates themselves from the fireman's shovelling. It also acts as the support to the baffle plate.

The baffle plate sits on the lip plate and its job is to direct the secondary air under the nose of the brick arch and onto the firebed. The reason for using a baffle plate to direct the air in this manner is that, if not properly directed, cold air entering the firebox above the fire can set up severe stresses in the firebox tubeplate and in so doing bring about leaking tubes. Subsequent chapters will deal with the tubes themselves.

When dealing with the steam locomotive there are always anomalies or variations to consider, and one such variation is to be found on locomotives of the former London and North Eastern Railway. Former LNER engines have a lip plate and baffle plate incorporated into the firehole door itself. When firing these engines, one 'fired through the flap', a term which meant the main firehole door was left closed. This was well enough in theory given small coals, but large lumps of coal would not pass through the flap arrangement and the whole door would have to be opened in order to fire with large coals.

When firing 'by the book', large lumps were supposed to be broken up using the coal pick but human nature being what it is this practice was not always strictly adhered to. This is perhaps a convenient point to say a few words about the fireman's skills in managing his fire, water and boiler pressure.

There are a great many variables which affect the way in which the steam locomotive is fired; it is far more than simply shovelling coal. The fireman has under his control the thickness of the firebed, the volume of primary and secondary air being fed to the fire, the size of the coals added

to the fire, the rate at which water is admitted to the boiler and, to a lesser extent, the amount of draught upon the fire. Other factors which affect the firing of the locomotive are the weight of the train, the gradient and the cut-off and regulator opening; even the weather has its effects.

In copybook firing, fist-sized coals would be added to a bright fire of about six to eight inches in thickness, each additional shovelful being fired to the brightest spots in the firebed. The reason for firing to the bright spots is that these are the areas where the firebed is thinnest. The thinner the firebed, the more air that passed through and the brighter the fire.

Theory is one thing, practice another. In service the fireman would tend to keep the fire thickest at the back of the firebox tapering toward the front. On a locomotive with a wide firebox the fireman would keep the back corners well filled and the fire well built up just under the firehole door, and only the very biggest lumps of coal would be broken up with the coal pick.

To return to the construction of the firebox, we have covered how it is made up of plates of steel and copper and how these plates are held together and secured against the pressure of the steam by the use of stays. We have mentioned some of the other items which are incorporated into the firebox; the brick arch, the fusible plugs, fire grate, foundation ring, lip plate and baffle plate. These items are what might be described as the internal fixtures and fittings of the firebox. However, they are not the only items in the construction of the firebox of the steam locomotive.

The external plates of the firebox carry the washout plugs and the mudhole doors and these items along with the handholes — a mudhole on the upper quadrant of the firebox — give access to the water space between the inner and outer firebox. Just as a kettle builds up an inner coating of scale, so too does the steam locomotive. This build-up of scale not only reduces the steaming efficiency of the boiler, it also causes serious damage to the firebox. The scale is percolated around the firebox by the boiling water and as it travels around the water space it scours the plates and wastes the stays. The way in which this problem is tackled is by washing out the water space at regular intervals, and by using water

This overhead view of Riddles Standard Class 7 Pacific No 70000 *Britannia* shows the safety valves — with just a gentle 'feather' emerging — sited ahead of the firebox on the first ring of the boiler. Note the steam manifold on top of the firebox.

softening treatment. The task of washing out is performed by utilising the washout plugs, mud-hole doors and handholes (sometimes referred to as skyholes). Copious quantities of water are used to swill out the scale and a variety of rods are used to dislodge scale so that the whole water space is cleared.

Two rows of washout plugs are located along the outside of the firebox: one above the level of the crown plate and on the backplate of the firebox on the locomotive's footplate; the other above the foundation ring on the lower section of the firebox. Washout plugs are also located on the upper quadrant of the boiler barrel, the smokebox tubeplate and the throatplate.

These plugs and covers also allow inspection of the water space by the boiler inspector. By using a lighted taper and a mirror it is possible for the boiler inspector to ascertain the level of scouring of the firebox plates and wasting of the stays and also to see that there are no broken stays — though the main check for broken stays is by tapping them with a hammer and listening to the sound they make.

Another fitting most usually located on the exterior of the firebox is the safety valves, though not all locomotives have the safety valves in this position. Many of the engines of the Great Western and the Bulleid Pacifics of the Southern are probably the most numerous and noteworthy exceptions to this rule. In the case of these loco-motives the safety valves are located on the first ring of the boiler barrel.

The safety valves are an important feature in the safety of not only the locomotive but also the general public — a boiler explosion in a crowded station could be devastating. In the early days of steam, boiler explosions were not commonplace, but they did occur and as the railway network began to grow so too did the frequency of explosions.

The earliest forms of safety valves were not only mechanically fairly crude they were also open to abuse. Primitive safety valves could be screwed down by the driver or have their balance weights shifted so that safe boiler pressure was exceeded. Most probably this was the consequence of either a lack of knowledge or because the inefficient locomotive could only be made to

fulfil its task if the boiler pressure were increased by tampering with the valves.

In modern locomotive practice the footplate crew are no longer able to alter the setting of the safety valve. Indeed they can now be set only by being removed from the locomotive, the new pressure settings being made in the fitting shop.

Two types of valve have been used in practice, one a variant of a valve initially designed by John Ramsbottom of the London and North Western Railway. The early type of Ramsbottom safety valve incorporated a handle that the driver could operate, to release steam but not exceed boiler pressure. However, the variant widely used in British locomotive practice, especially by the GWR, did not have that lever. The other exten-sively used design was the Ross 'pop' valve. This valve was widely in use in LNER locomotives and is characterised by suddenly bursting into life and closing with equal brevity, hence the term 'pop'. The Ramsbottom valve was more of a sizzler, recognisable by its 'white feather' of steam and often to be seen on Stanier's engines.

There are a couple of items of firebox furniture which we have yet to cover. One is the firebox combustion chamber, the other the thermic siphon. By no means all locomotives are fitted with either or both of these items. The firebox combustion chamber is essentially a space above and behind the brick arch created by setting back the firebox tubeplate further into the boiler barrel, thus extending the area of the firebox.

The idea behind the combustion chamber is to gain the maximum heat energy from the burning of the volatile gases given off in the burning of the coal. This design feature was of particular use when hard coals, which burn more quickly than soft Welsh coals, were the locomotive's regular fuel supply. Locomotives fitted with this form of firebox construction include the Royal Scots, their near neighbours, the Lord Nelson class of the Southern Railway and the Gresley Pacifics to name just a few of the more well known types so fitted.

There is a little nmemonic concerning the products of burning coal — NO CASH; this is Nitrogen, Oxygen, Carbon, Ash, Sulphur and Hydrogen. The heat-producing elements within this mixture are the carbon and hydrogen. Coal is approximately 75% carbon and also contains about 5% hydrogen, 10% ash, 8% oxygen with just traces of sulphur (0.5%) and nitrogen (1.5%) making up the remaining constituents.

To obtain the heat from the carbon and hydrogen in the coal, the coal must be burned in air and a temperature in excess of eight hundred degrees fahrenheit is needed to achieve this. To burn the coal efficiently the temperature must be considerably higher — in the order of two thousand, five hundred degrees. To burn one pound of coal, about twelve pounds of air are needed to ensure the proper combustion of the 'volatiles' — the gaseous matter given off when coal is burned — and the fixed carbon, coke. Of this twelve pounds of air, approximately nine pounds are nitrogen which plays no part in the combustion process, except as a restriction on it (indeed, the nitrogen detracts from the combustion process by absorbing heat which might otherwise heat up the water). Further heat loss occurs due to the fact that the exhaust gases going up the chimney are still in the region of seven hundred and fifty degrees fahrenheit.

Heat loss in the combustion process also occurs when too much or too little air is admitted to the grate and when too much or too little coal is added to the firebed. When too little air and too much coal are added to the firebed thick black smoke — 'clag' — is what ensues. If the firebed is too thin and too much cold air is admitted the heat loss is still there, but this time there is no smoke. The ideal to aim for is a light grey exhaust from the chimney top indicating that the right mix of coal and air is being achieved and the maximum benefit is being derived from the fuel being burned.

Unlike the combustion chamber, the thermic siphon does not alter the area in which heat is generated but it does increase the available heating surface. The thermic siphon is created by plates attached to the firebox crown plate and the lower section of the firebox tubeplate (see diagram). The construction of the siphon has a twofold effect: it helps in the circulation of the boiler water and passes this circulating water through the hottest part of the firebox and is therefore an additional part of the total heating surface, in the area of highest temperature. The boilers of the Bulleid Pacifics are fitted with thermic siphons and this is one probable reason for their well-attested steaming capability.

In locomotives fitted with thermic siphons the brick arch is fitted between the plates of the siphon, and in locomotives which incorporate a firebox combustion chamber there is also the possibility of incorporating a siphon into this space, as is shown in the second diagram.

The advent of the thermic siphon was one of the last refinements, in British locomotive practice, of the steam locomotive firebox/boiler, a development process which had spanned one hundred and fifty years, from rivetted and stayed plates of wrought iron and copper to an all-welded steel construction, replete with thermic siphons.

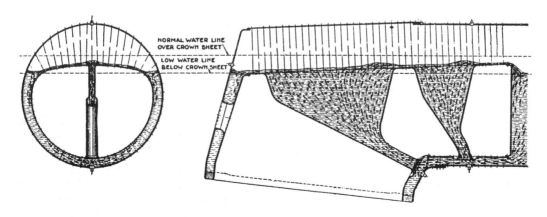

NORMAL WATER LINE OVER CROWN SHEET

LOW WATER LINE BELOW CROWN SHEET

A firebox and combustion chamber fitted with a thermic syphon.

CHAPTER 2

Boilers, Clacks and Domes

This second chapter will concentrate on the boiler barrel and its associated 'hangers-on': injectors, domes, clacks, manifolds and whistles. The boiler, as I'm sure everyone knows, is the barrel-shaped bit which fits between the firebox and the smokebox. Boilers may be parallel, tapered or vertical and as we have already mentioned in Chapter One there have been several experimental designs: high pressure marine types and those with water-tube fireboxes, such as some of the early locomotives on the Stockton and Darlington Railway. The only other type of boiler which was tried in any numbers in twentieth century British Railway practice was the Franco-Crosti design fitted to a batch of the BR Class 9F 2-10-0s, Nos 92022 to 92029.

The boiler is, generally, constructed from mild steel and in the case of the taper boiler the construction is in two sections, the large diameter rear section being attached to the firebox outer wrapper. The front section of the boiler is the point where the water supply from the injectors enters the boiler — the 'top feed' — but before we come to dealing with the injectors and the supply of water to the boiler, a fuller description of the boiler itself is necessary.

Inside the barrel of the boiler are a number of components: the smoke or flue tubes, the injector delivery pipes and/or trays, the main internal steam pipe, the steam manifold collecting pipe and the longitudinal stays, referred to in Chapter One. Inside the large flue/smoke tubes are the superheater elements/tubes, if the locomotive is fitted with this device.

This is perhaps a good point to make the distinction between the saturated steam and super-

heated steam types of design. The smoke tube superheater was first introduced into British locomotive design by the Lancashire & Yorkshire Railway in 1906, though the invention itself was brought about by a Herr Schmidt and was first used on German Railways in 1898.

Prior to these dates all locomotive boilers were of the saturated steam type (though some classes were later re-designed to incorporate superheating). What is superheating? Superheating is a process which dries and heats the steam before it passes to the cylinders — in crude terms superheated steam delivers more 'umph' by volume than saturated steam. This allows greater use to be made, not only of the heat generated by the burning of coals but also of the expansive properties of the steam.

Superheated steam differs from saturated steam in the fact that its temperature is independent of its pressure, since at any pressure it may have any temperature — unlike saturated steam which has a different temperature for each difference in pressure. Saturated steam at a boiler pressure of 175 psi has a temperature of 370 degrees, at a boiler pressure of 250 psi the temperature is 400 degrees. These temperatures are effectively the boiling point of the water in the boiler operating at those pressures. Lower the steam pressure and the boiling point is lowered too. By way of an aside, if you boil water up a mountain the boiling point is at less than 212 degrees because the air pressure is lower the higher the altitude.

Saturated steam contains many small droplets of water. What happens in superheating is that these very small water droplets are also turned into steam. You might describe superheating as a process of steam drying. This process has the effect of raising the actual volume of steam by increasing the efficiency of evaporation. In rounded numbers there is a one third rise in the volume of steam for every ten per cent rise in its temperature, and the rise in temperature from saturated to superheated steam varies with the size and number of superheater elements.

In locomotive development, engines which have begun life as indifferent steamers have been transformed by alterations to the number of superheater elements incorporated in their construction. One classic example about which much has been written and said is the Stanier Jubilee class, though it must be added that almost as much improvement was gained through alterations to the height and diameter of the blastpipe. The superheater is not a cure-all for poor steaming locomotives, but it has often proved a benefit. However, there have been instances of locomotives fitted with superheaters subsequently having them removed. One such was the Wilson Worsdell J27 0-6-0 of the North Eastern Railway, one of which has been preserved and restored to working order by the North Eastern Locomotive Preservation Group.

A very rough rule of thumb when working out whether or not a locomotive is superheated is to look at the size of the dome — the taller the dome the more likely it is that the engine is of the saturated steam type. Broadly speaking most locomotives designed and built after the First World War are of the superheated variety, though as with all things steam there are the exceptions, the famous LMS Jinty 0-6-0T being one. To be fair though the Jinty was, with a

The Fowler 3F 0-6-0 tank, commonly — if incorrectly — known as the 'Jinty', is an example of a locomotive built after the First World War with a non-superheated (saturated) boiler. By this time, the use of superheating was commonplace throughout Britain's railway companies, but the 3F was a little-modified variation of a Victorian Midland Railway design. One of several surviving examples of the class, the Severn Valley Railway's No 47383 comes off shed at Bridgnorth.

few modifications, based on a pre-war Midland Railway design, even though the class was not constructed until the early 1920s.

In a saturated steam engine the regulator valve(s) and main internal steam pipe are situated in the dome, which is the highest and driest part of the boiler, though in the early days of steam locomotion the construction, placement and operation of the regulator was something of a lottery, with numerous different types and locations being used. However, in the case of twentieth century locomotive practice, the dome was the preferred location for the regulator valve in saturated steam locomotives.

In superheated engines the dome is no longer the highest driest point of the boiler — this is now the exit side of the superheater header. The net effect of this has tended to be a lowering of the dome and in some instances a repositioning of the regulator valve, which is relocated to a point adjacent to the superheater header on the smoke-box side of the front tubeplate. Although this practice may make some sense from a design point of view it was unpopular with maintenance staff and some difficulties arose as a result.

Another factor which accounts for a lowered dome is the use of a horizontal, as opposed to a vertical, regulator valve in those locomotives which retain the dome position regulator valves. I use the term valves, plural, because there are two valves in the construction of the regulator, first or pilot/starting valve and 'full' second valve. There were even some locomotives fitted with multiple valve regulators. The multi-valve regulator was situated in the superheater header and the object was to obtain a fine regulation of the steam flow.

There were two options in siting the regulator valve within the superheater header: on the inflow side or the outflow side and, railways being railways, both types were employed. This type of regulator had a small pilot/starting valve and then there were up to four main valves, cam-opened by a lever operated from the cab just as the more standard type of regulator is also lever-operated from the footplate.

The use of multi-valve regulators fitted in the superheater was very much a post-war development and, not unsurprisingly, there are still examples of locomotives in preservation fitted with this form of regulator: the Peppercorn development of Thompson's Class A2 Pacific No 60532 *Blue Peter* is one and the unique No 71000 *Duke of Gloucester* is another. The two survivors of R. A. Riddles' Britannia Class are also locomotives fitted with this type of regulator.

While on the subject of regulators and regulator valves it may be useful at this juncture to explain what is called 'the passage of steam'. This is the jargon for what happens when the regulator is opened. On the opening of the regulator, steam from the boiler is admitted to the main internal steam pipe. In the case of the superheated locomotive, it then enters the saturated side of the superheater header. From there it travels through the superheater elements/tubes to end up on the superheated side of the superheater header. On leaving the superheater header it travels via the main steam pipe to the steam chest from where it enters the cylinder through whichever port is open.

In the case of the saturated steam engine, the steam travels direct from the regulator valve via the main internal steam pipe to the steam chest and thence to the cylinder via whichever port is open. With the regulator open, the steam chest is constantly full of steam and the valves which are located within the steam chest determine the volume of steam admitted to the cylinder, but more on this in a later chapter.

To return to the construction of the locomotive boiler and its associated parts, we were discussing superheating and what it is. The superheater header is simply a large casting with an inflow and outflow side. The superheater elements, which are a series of tubes which fold and return upon themselves, as can be seen from the diagram, mate with holes in either side of the casting. These elements create one continuous system in which saturated steam flows in at one side and superheated steam flows out on the other, after travelling back and forth inside the elements. The elements are sited inside the large smoke/ flue tubes and are surrounded by the hot gases being drawn off the fire by the vacuum created in the smokebox by the exhaust steam or the blower. It is these hot gases, which have already helped in boiling the water, which help to dry the

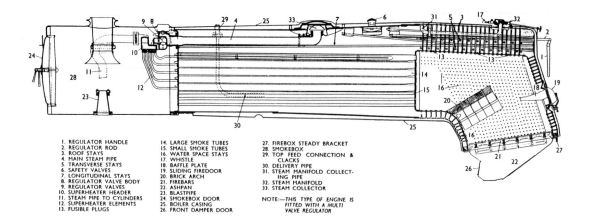

1. REGULATOR HANDLE	14. LARGE SMOKE TUBES	27. FIREBOX STEADY BRACKET
2. REGULATOR ROD	15. SMALL SMOKE TUBES	28. SMOKEBOX
3. ROOF STAYS	16. WATER SPACE STAYS	29. TOP FEED CONNECTION &
4. MAIN STEAM PIPE	17. WHISTLE	CLACKS
5. TRANSVERSE STAYS	18. BAFFLE PLATE	30. DELIVERY PIPE
6. SAFETY VALVES	19. SLIDING FIREDOOR	31. STEAM MANIFOLD COLLECT-
7. LONGITUDINAL STAYS	20. BRICK ARCH	ING PIPE
8. REGULATOR VALVE BODY	21. FIREBARS	32. STEAM MANIFOLD
9. REGULATOR VALVES	22. ASHPAN	33. STEAM COLLECTOR
10. SUPERHEATER HEADER	23. BLASTPIPE	
11. STEAM PIPE TO CYLINDERS	24. SMOKEBOX DOOR	NOTE:—THIS TYPE OF ENGINE IS
12. SUPERHEATER ELEMENTS	25. BOILER CASING	FITTED WITH A MULTI
13. FUSIBLE PLUGS	26. FRONT DAMPER DOOR	VALVE REGULATOR

SECTIONAL VIEW OF BOILER WITH SUPERHEATER

Cross-section of a typical superheated boiler, identifying the key components and their relationships. Note the positioning of the multi-valve regulator adjacent to the superheater header, and the siting of the top feed to the boiler, with its associated clack valves, on the front ring of the boiler.

steam flowing round the superheater.

In our description of the boiler, a little historical background to its development would not go amiss. Some of the early Stephenson locomotives had only one flue tube and were pretty indifferent steamers. The early Trevithick engines were of the return flue type, mentioned in Chapter One, as were the first developments — some might say improvements — of Stephenson's locomotives by Hackworth, the man appointed by Stephenson as locomotive superintendent of the Stockton and Darlington Railway's workshops at Shildon. Hackworth's own entry in the Rainhill trials, *Sans Pareil*, used this innovation.

The net effect of the return flue was that as the hot gases passed through a flue from the firebox through the boiler and back again to return to exhaust via the chimney, more of the heat they carried was passed to the water in the boiler. This not only raised efficiency but also improved the steaming qualities of a boiler which was, at this time, still providing steam for a non-expansion engine, that is one which worked by admission. These two terms, admission and expansion, will be more fully explained in a later chapter.

This use of the return flue may seem to have been a small step but it was an important one from the point of gaining the maximum in efficiency from all the heat being given off in the combustion process. It was certainly a recognition of the ability to derive more heat energy from the exhaust gases. Overcoming heat loss and creating an increase in the heating surface was one of the early pioneers' prime concerns and it was achieving this which eventually secured the success of the steam locomotive.

The winner at Rainhill, *Rocket,* as we mentioned in Chapter One, was constructed with a multi-tubed boiler, first patented in 1826 by James Neville, and it was this type of boiler which dominated in the years after 1830. A modern locomotive will have both large and small tubes, with the large tubes being the location for the elements of the superheater system. The small tubes were the norm until the advent of superheating and they may be referred to as the smoke tubes and the large tubes as the superheater tubes, though in practice smoke and hot gases pass through both.

Another difference between the boiler of a modern locomotive and that of its Victorian counterpart is that in the early locomotives the boiler often provided the rigid strength of the locomotive, not the frame as in a modern locomotive. In a modern locomotive the frame acts as a carrier to the boiler, in early locomotives, the boiler is the hanger for the frame. However, perhaps the single most important difference between old and new boilers or fireboxes is that the number of plates of metal needed for the construction of these items is substantially less in the modern locomotive. Steel-making technology rather than locomotive development provided the ability to modify design practice.

History aside, we have thus far considered those items invisible to the naked eye, the internal fixtures of the boiler. A couple of the items mentioned deserve a little more by way of explanation: the injector delivery pipe and the steam manifold collection pipe.

The injector delivery pipe delivers cold water from the tender to the lowest part of the boiler or the part farthest from the heat source. The cold water mixes with the coldest of the water already in the boiler. In simple terms this helps with the circulation and percolation of water and is the least stressful in relation to temperature differences between the boiler and firebox. The cold water in this description is not absolutely cold as in passing through the injector its temperature will have been raised by approximately one hundred degrees fahrenheit. However, this is still relatively cold in relation to the temperature of the water in the boiler.

The way in which the water is admitted to the boiler can vary. Sometimes the delivery pipe passes through the water space to vent in the lower part of the boiler; another method is to have the delivery pipe discharge into a series of trays. The overall aim is to try and avoid cold water from the tender entering the boiler at a point where it would mix with boiling water and set up stress in the metal. There are one or two other aspects to consider: one is the trapping of impurities in the water and another the dissolving of free oxygen in the water — this latter helps to reduce corrosion through oxidisation.

The steam manifold collection pipe feeds steam to the main manifold on the locomotive footplate. It is the source for the steam to do things like operate the blower, injectors, steam brake, ejector, train heating, whistle, etc. This pipe is located in the area of the boiler which is known as the steam space, often in close proximity to the dome area. This ensures that the steam is the hottest and driest available. The manifold collection pipe is located in the dome

Clearly showing its Swindon pedigree, with Belpaire firebox and taper boiler, is Riddles Standard Class 4MT 4-6-0 No 75069. Note the double chimney, and the injectors, positioned on the fireman's side of the locomotive cab.

area whether or not the locomotive is fitted with a superheater.

Moving on from the internal aspects of the boiler, on the outside we have the 'clacks' and the whistle. The clacks are essentially a non-return valve — they are pushed open by the water being delivered by the injector and forced shut by the steam pressure in the boiler once the injector is turned off.

The whistle, which may be found anywhere between the cab front and the chimney, is a warning device and, for a good many people, a form of identification. A serious afficionado would recognise whether the locomotive was of LMS or LNER origins just from the note of the whistle. In addition to being a warning device, the whistle is also a means of communication and whole books of whistle codes were once used on different occasions and for widely differing purposes from warning the signalman that you were a runaway, to indicating which route you wanted to take, or telling the driver of a banking engine that you were ready to start the train.

Rumour has it that the whistle came about quite by chance. According to legend, Stephenson introduced the whistle following a collision between one of his locomotives and a wagonload of eggs and butter. Stephenson had been involved in the Leicester & Swannington Railway and an official of the L & S, one Ashlin Bagster, suggested to Stephenson that the incorporation of some sort of steam-driven whistle might help warn people of the approach of a train. The locomotive involved in the accident, *Samson* was fitted with a steam whistle made by a musical instrument maker from Leicester.

Whilst it is undoubtedly true that the whistle was a great leap forward in safety, a more mundane but equally important development, which owed nothing to butter, eggs or farm carts, was the clack or non-return valve. Generally speaking, the clacks are located forward of the dome on the upper quadrant of the boiler barrel or are incorporated with the dome or safety valves, as they often are in GWR practice, into what is referred to as a 'top feed' arrangement. Thus, in some designs the clacks are mounted alongside the dome and covered (as is the rest of the boiler) by cladding and lagging; in some they are not. In

other words sometimes you see them, sometimes you don't. We shall say a little more about the clacks when we come to deal with the operations of the injectors later in this chapter.

Between the visible sheeting of the boiler and the boiler itself is the lagging/cladding. In days gone by the material for the lagging was asbestos; today the material used is rockwool. It does the same job but without the poisonous aspects of the asbestos. The lagging helps retain heat while the engine is working and it also helps in reducing stress in the cooling down process when the locomotive is taken out of steam.

Having now outlined the various pieces of hardware which constitute the locomotive boiler, it may be pertinent to cover some of the jargon and terminology associated with the boiler's function as a part in the whole.

One of the most often referred to problems is that of 'priming'. Priming is the term which describes what happens when water is drawn into the cylinders with the steam. When water is boiling it bubbles and effervesces. If the boiler water level is very high the bubbles of water can be lifted by the steam into the regulator valve and then carried by the 'passage of steam' into the pistons — and from there out of the chimney with the exhaust steam. The results of priming are, generally speaking, nothing worse than water droplets being emitted with the exhaust; however, in severe cases of priming serious damage can be caused.

The sort of damage which a bad case of priming can bring about ranges from damage to piston packings/glands through bent motion to smashed cylinder covers — you cannot compress water in the same way you can steam. The usual method of stopping a dose of priming is to open the cylinder cocks and/or close the regulator. However, in severe cases of priming closing the regulator is not always possible as the escaping boiler water prevents the regulator valve reseating.

This difficulty in closing the regulator valve is sometimes referred to as 'hydraulicing': i.e. the pistons begin to act almost like a pump sucking water from the boiler and thereby accentuating the problem. It must be said that dirty water can also be a cause of priming and that the gradient of the track can be a contributory factor.

A view along the boiler of Collett GWR Castle Class 7P 4-6-0 No 5080 *Defiant*, illustrating the steampipe to the outside cylinders, top feed and the distinctive Swindon safety-valve bonnet.

When running downhill with only a small regulator opening the boiler water level appears to be less than it is. If the gradient changes to an uphill one and the regulator is opened further, to maintain momentum, the water level over the firebox and rear portion of the boiler rises, often with a surge, and this can result in priming in much the same way as over-filling the boiler. Similarly, blowing off can also create priming as the escaping steam draws the water up with it carrying droplets into the regulator valve as it does so. These then are the major causes of priming and an explanation of the term itself.

In the early days of locomotive construction, priming was quite a serious technical problem and various means were adopted in attempts to overcome it. In some locomotives two separate domes were used, one acting as a collector for the other. One ingenious development was not unlike the Schmidt smoke tube superheater and may conceivably be described as the precursor to it. An 0-4-2 built by Hawthorn & Co. for the Newcastle and North Shields Railway in 1840 had a steam chamber in the smokebox through which passed a series of tubes which carried the firebox gases out to exhaust. Thus steam which was bound for the cylinders passed around these heated pipes being dried, or superheated in the process.

The early development of the steam locomotive lacked little by way of innovative and clever ideas. The real difficulty was a lack of technology. Or to put it another way the ideas of the designers and builders were ahead of the materials available to them and on occasions they were forced to improvise entirely as a result of the shortcomings of available materials.

To complete the description of the boiler we need to look at the operation of the clacks in conjunction with the injectors. How is the injector able to force water into the boiler against the pressure of steam using that self-same steam as the source of its own power? To answer this question we need to look at what takes place in the injector body when steam and water are admitted to it.

There are several types of injector: lifting or non lifting, live steam or exhaust steam. The difference between live and exhaust steam injectors is that the one uses steam direct from the boiler while the other, the exhaust steam injector, operates by using spent steam from the cylinders and as a result will only work when the engine is in motion with the regulator open.

The difference in these two types of injector, the exhaust and live steam types, is the shape, position and size of the injector cones. Inside the body of the injector are a series of cones, which in crude terms do the following: create a vacuum, combine steam with water and turn velocity into

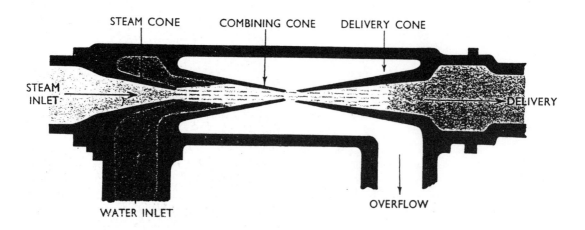

SIMPLE INJECTOR

The 'cone' principle fundamental to the operation of the injectors.

pressure. This is true for both live or exhaust steam types; only the cones differ because of the different pressures and temperatures of the two types of steam. The exhaust injector may also incorporate a supplementary live steam supply which will keep it operating if the regulator is closed or the volume of exhaust steam becomes insufficient to maintain its operation.

The steam passing through the steam cone creates a vacuum which then draws in water in an attempt to fill the abhorrent vacuum. Thus the water and steam are mixed and given velocity. A very simple analogy is the garden hose. With a hose of large diameter water merely pours from the end when the tap is opened. However if you restrict the end of the pipe, pressure builds up behind the restriction and the result is a jet of water from the pipe instead of the trickle.

The next stage in the operation of the injector is to pass the accelerated steam/water mixture through another cone, this time one which opens outwards, in relation to the direction of the water flow. This has the effect of translating the previously acquired velocity into pressure. The result is a water/steam mixture with both a degree of velocity and a pressure greater than the original pressure of the steam and hence this pushes open the clack against the boiler pressure. The three cones which are involved in this process are generally referred to as the steam cone, the combining cone and the delivery cone.

It must be borne in mind that this is a very simplistic schema of what is going on. The diagrams show the shape of the cones and, as can be seen, the way in which the differing shapes of the cones impart velocity and then convert this velocity into pressure.

The construction of the working injector, as opposed to the 'model', incorporates various devices to improve its efficiency: to allow automatic switching between exhaust and live steam or to shut off the steam supply to allow work on the injectors to be carried out whilst the engine is in steam. However, despite these additions and modifications the basic principles remain constant.

The injectors themselves are, in general, mounted below the footplate in such a position as to allow easy access and to allow the fireman to see if they are operating (i.e. so the fireman can see the overflow pipe). If either steam or water are issuing from the overflow when the injector is being used this indicates to the fireman that the injector is not operating correctly.

In working the injector, first the water supply is opened and when water begins to run from the overflow the steam supply is turned on. This is where the expression 'picking up' comes from. The supply of steam, as described in an earlier paragraph, picks up the water. You might have heard a banging sound on occasions when the injector is turned on. This is caused by the injector cycling on and off and not 'picking up', or at least only partially doing so. The banging is the rapid opening and closing of the clack valve due to the steam/water mix from the injector being insufficient to overcome the boiler pressure.

Just as the injector has complications on the basic principles so too does the clack. The clack, in addition to being a non-return valve, also seals the boiler from the atmosphere and is in fact a double valve. Another feature in its construction is that it is 'winged'. This ensures that it re-seats in a different position with each operation and thus reduces wear in the faces and seats.

The initial method used to get water into the boiler was the feed water pump, and although it was used in the early days of locomotive construction, the feed water pump was not a major feature in British locomotive practice after 1860. The injector was invented in France in 1859, by a Monsieur Giffard, and its benefits were quickly seized upon. The British patent rights were taken up in 1860 by Sharp Stewart and from then on it was more or less no contest, injectors winning hands-down.

The feed water pumps were either crosshead or crank driven and their major drawback was that when the engine was stationary they didn't work. Other faults of this system were that at high speeds the pressure in the pumps often became quite excessive and failures resulted. Such were the benefits of the injector that once it had proved reliable the feed pump virtually disappeared, apart from the almost inevitable exceptions and an attempted revival by William Stroudley on some locomotives fitted with feed water heaters.

31

This then covers the main components of the boiler and its operations within the whole. In the next chapter we will look at the smokebox, blast-pipe, chimney and related components, and begin to look at how the steam is turned into motion.

CHAPTER 3

Blastpipes, Snifters and Petticoats

In the previous chapters we have touched on the function of the smokebox. Here we will be looking at those functions and at the other items of the locomotive's construction contained within or on the smokebox; blastpipe, blower-ring, snifting valves, chimney petticoat, steam pipes, etc. This will then lead us on to the point at which the steam pressure from the boiler becomes tractive effort at the wheels.

A brace of Great Western smokeboxes, displaying varieties of single and double chimneys. On the left, single chimney Collett Castle Class 7P 4-6-0 No 5029 *Nunney Castle*; on the right, double chimney King Class 8P 4-6-0 No 6024 *King Edward I*. The two 4-cylinder express locomotives were captured around the turntable at Old Oak Common during an open day in August 1991.

The smokebox, which is attached to the boiler barrel by a ring of rivets, is the last of the items concerned in the process of turning the heat derived from burning coals into steam to drive the pistons and then the wheels. The smokebox, with the exception of the chimney orifice, is air-tight and is the location for the locomotive's exhaust system — the arrangement of which comprises the blastpipe, which is attached to the exhaust steam outlets from the cylinders, the chimney petticoat which is attached to the lower portion of the chimney and the chimney itself.

The blastpipe is, despite its apparent simplicity, an important ingredient in determining the steaming capability of a locomotive. The height and the circumference of the blastpipe can both have their effects on the performance of the locomotive. Altering the height affects where in the grate area the coal is burned and the size of the orifice determines the ferocity of the blast and the extent or degree of the vacuum created by the escaping spent steam. In turn, this determines the strength and evenness of the pull on the fire.

The partial vacuum created in the smokebox by either the escaping exhaust steam, or by means of the 'blower', is what draws the fire: too fierce and 'fire chucking' will result, too weak and insufficient draught will mean too little air being drawn through the firebed resulting in poor combustion and heat loss and, as a consequence, poor steaming.

Nature abhors a vacuum and in order to destroy the vacuum in the smokebox, air is drawn through the firebed, where it is mixed with the combustible gases in the firebox, before being drawn down the smoke and flue tubes into the smokebox. The gases entering the smokebox from the flue/smoke tubes are drawn out through the chimney by the escaping exhaust steam from the cylinders, being evacuated to the atmosphere via the blastpipe. When the regulator is closed and no exhaust is being produced, the 'blower' provides a steam jet which substitutes for the exhaust steam from the cylinders.

The blower is controlled from the cab. The driver or fireman can operate a lever on the footplate which opens a steam valve that allows steam from the boiler to be substituted for the exhaust steam. The blower is a vital piece of equipment and, if it fails to operate, the locomotive has to be withdrawn from service until it can be repaired.

The failure of the blower means that any down-draught caused when passing under a bridge or tunnel would force smoke and flame out through the firehole, a situation known as a 'blowback' and a very dangerous one. (This happened to the King Arthur Class 4-6-0 No. 777 *Sir Lamiel* while working one of the North Wales Coast Expresses during 1991. A fractured steam supply to the blower caused the engine to be taken off the train at Chester.)

In the smokebox, the steam pipe controlled by the blower valve in the cab is turned into a ring of small jets located around the top of the blastpipe. The blastpipe itself can be single, double or, as in the case of the Bulleid-designed engines (and some of the engines Bulleid modified) they can be multiple.

The blastpipe is really just another name for an exhaust pipe and, just as motor manufacturers experiment with or modify the exhaust systems on their sportier models, so locomotive engineers experiment with the blastpipes to improve the performance or reduce coal consumption, or both, of the steam locomotive.

The creation of a smokebox vacuum by the use of the exhaust steam, to create a draught on the fire being exhausted via a blastpipe in the smokebox and thus creating the vacuum, was not quite as clear-cut an idea as it may appear. In the single or return flue type of boiler/firebox arrangement such as was used in the earliest locomotives, a blastpipe arrangement would, and did, result in 'fire chucking'. That is the blast was such that fire was pulled out of the firebox and up into the smokestack.

There are a variety of conflicting arguments as to just who was responsible for the incorporation of a blastpipe and who discovered, or made most specific use of, the notion of the smokebox blast-pipe and its vacuum-creating potential. In some way or other all the early pioneers are in with a shout, with Trevithick and Hackworth just possibly a nose in front. What is beyond dispute is that the idea and use of such a device was in existence at the dawn of steam locomotion and its refinement and development has had quite a deal of impact on locomotive design, performance and appearance throughout the entire period of steam locomotive history.

In addition to the previously mentioned variants of the blastpipe there are such innovations as the jumper blastpipe, an arrangement which provides for an increase in the area of the blastpipe orifice relative to the force and frequency of the exhaust stroke, an arrangement much favoured by the GWR. It was the use by Stanier, himself an ex-Great Western man, of the jumper blast-pipe for his Jubilee class which contributed to their early steaming difficulties.

The Kylchap double blastpipe and the Giesl ejector are two other variants which were used to good effect — the former being particularly noteworthy in relation to improved performance of Gresley's Pacifics, whilst the latter has proved beneficial in service in the Bulleid West Country Class 4-6-2 No. 34092 *City of Wells*.

The Giesl ejector is a system of parallel nozzles which replace the conventional blastpipe. The nozzles are laid out in an oblong shape — which gives the chimney its characteristic long narrow appearance. The effect of the Giesl ejector is to provide a free flow exhaust passage for the steam and an increased and more even draught on the fire. In practice the Giesl ejector has increased the locomotive's power output, in some instances by as much as 20 percent. Alas this and other efficiency improvements came about too late in the day to save the steam locomotive as a means of motive power on Britain's railways.

The Kylchap system was based on the idea of streamlining, which was very popular in the

Bulleid Southern Railway West Country Class 7P5F Pacific No 34092 *City of Wells*, **an example of a preserved locomotive which has benefited from the fitting of a Giesl ejector in the place of the usual blastpipe and chimney. The 'West Country' makes a volcanic exit from London's Marylebone Station with a railtour for Stratford-upon-Avon in November 1986. Note the 'Golden Arrow' regalia. No 34092 is currently undergoing overhaul on the Keighley and Worth Valley Railway.**

1930s, and was the product of co-operation between French locomotive designer Chapelon and the Finnish technician Kyala, hence the name Kylchap. Chapelon believed that just as it was important to streamline the exterior of the locomotive it was equally important to streamline the steam passages, so that the exhaust steam had the smoothest possible flow out of the cylinder and up through the blastpipe.

In the locomotive departments there was also an oft-used but an officially disliked innovation called the 'jimmy' (or as some titled them 'jemmys'). The 'Jimmy' consists of two, or occasionally just one, strip(s) of metal placed across the blastpipe opening in the form of a cross. This device restricts the flow of exhaust steam from the cylinders and has the effect of increasing the pull on the fire. In a way it fools the engine into thinking it's working harder than it really is — and thus the 'Jimmy'' would, in some cases, help a poor steaming locomotive steam more freely by improving the draught on the fire. However, the 'Jimmy' was officially frowned upon and its use today on main-line certified locomotives is banned as being an item of non-standard equipment.

Because the smokebox and blastpipe arrangement has such a critical effect on the locomotive's steaming capabilities it is worth noting that it is not only experimentation with various types of blastpipe that has taken place, but also experimentation with the diameter of the blastpipe orifice and its height in relation to the transverse centre line of the smokebox tubeplate.

In addition to the blastpipe's relationship in creating draught on the fire, its diameter also affects the back-pressure in the cylinder, which if it is too great will restrict the free running of the engine and affect its maximum speed. The height of the blastpipe affects which area of the grate consumes the fuel most rapidly. Raising the height of the blastpipe increases the rate of combustion in the front portion of the grate.

Above the blastpipe is the chimney petticoat, so-called because this is what it looks like — a petticoat. The petticoat is attached to the lower section of the chimney and the chimney itself is the only exit to the atmosphere from what is an otherwise airtight vessel — the smokebox.

Some locomotives, particularly BR Standard classes, are fitted with what is termed a 'self-cleaning' smokebox, usually denoted by the letters SC carried just below the shed plate on the smokebox door. When a locomotive is in service particles of ash, partly burnt coal, and small unburnable impurities in the coal, are drawn by the draught through the tubes into the smokebox. These small pieces of char begin to pile up against the smokebox door, often causing the characteristic burn marks on the lower quarter of the smokebox door. (The other major cause of the burn marks is that the smokebox door seal is leaking air.) By way of an aside, it is these ash particles which damage and score the tubes and tubeplates. They also drop on top of the brick arch reducing its efficiency.

The self-cleaning smokebox was designed to overcome the problem of the build-up of ash. It is made up of an arrangement of plates and wire mesh screens. Plates are fitted across the end of the smokebox tubeplate which even out the draught through the tubes and deflect the ash particles to the lower part of the smokebox. The particles are then drawn back through the wire screens by the gas flow created by the escaping exhaust and the vacuum, before entering the exhaust from the blastpipe. This arrangement ensures that the particles which are ejected from the smokebox are cold and that they do not settle on the bottom of the smokebox.

Speaking from experience, the design works reasonably well but there is still some smokebox ash to be cleared — though much less than in locomotives not fitted with this device. As innovations go, the self-cleaning smokebox was a fairly late-in-the-day experiment, being used extensively only in locomotives built after the Second World War.

The smokebox is also the point of exhaust for the steam from the ejector. The ejector is the device which creates the vacuum in the train pipe for keeping the brakes off — there will be more on this in one of the later chapters. The steam used in creating this vacuum in the train pipe is exhausted into the smokebox. The smokebox was chosen not for any particular reason but simply because it is a convenient location.

The preceding chapter covered the superheater

A typical British 'front end', as displayed by Stanier LMS Class 5MT 4-6-0 No 45428 as it stands under the coaling plant at Grosmont on the North Yorkshire Moors Railway. Note the steampipe leading to the cylinders, and the couplings and hoses. No 45428, which is currently out-of-traffic, carries a 55A shedplate, indicating a Leeds Holbeck locomotive.

header which is also located in the smokebox, as too is the regulator on some locomotives. Other items of smokebox furnishings are the snifting valve and the steam pipes to as well as from the cylinders.

The snifting valve is either attached to the saturated side of the superheater header or in other instances to the steam chest. The snifting valve, also known as an anti-vacuum valve, is fitted to superheated locomotives to prevent, in particular, the overheating of the superheater elements. It allows air to be drawn into the cylinders when the engine is coasting with regulator closed. This in turn prevents ash and char being drawn into the cylinders and the air circulated via this means, through the super-heater, cylinders and blastpipe helps to cool the superheater elements when they are not full of

circulating steam, as they are with the regulator open.

The main steam pipe, which comes either from the regulator valve in the dome or from the superheated side of the superheater header, is another of the items visible in the smokebox. This pipe, as its name suggests, is for the supply of steam to the steam chests from which steam is admitted to the cylinders through whichever of the valve ports is open.

Effectively we have now covered the essential features of the firebox, boiler and smokebox and the factors involved in turning coal and water into the motive power of steam. We now arrive at the point of how that steam is transmitted from the boiler to the cylinder and how that in turn drives the wheels.

CHAPTER 4

Lap, Lead and the Steam Chest

We have already discussed in an earlier chapter what happens when the regulator is opened, in as much as an explanation of how the steam in the boiler is moved from the boiler to the steam chest. What we will now begin to look at is what happens once the steam enters the steam chest en route to the cylinder. I will leave until the following chapter the description of the valve gear assembly and power train, connecting and coupling rods, eccentrics, expansion links and related components.

The admission to and exhaust of steam from the cylinders is controlled by valves, just as admission of petrol or expulsion of exhaust from the cylinder is in an internal combustion engine. Various forms of valve gear have been experimented with, not only in the internal combustion engine but also in the steam engine. However, the valves of whatever type all have to fulfil a basic set of criteria. They must allow live steam to be admitted, allow a period for the expansion of the steam (more on this when we come to discuss 'cut-off'), open a passage for the exhaust steam, provide a compression interval when the valve has closed and admit lead steam before the piston commences its work stroke.

The duties performed by the valves to achieve the above criteria are to cover both steam ports when the valve is in the mid position, admit steam to only one end of the cylinder at a time, and open to exhaust at one end of the cylinder at least as soon as it opens to admit steam at the other.

The two main types of valves in use in British locomotive practice are the slide valve and the piston valve (see diagram) and there are four major terms connected with the valves: lap and lead, and inside or outside admission. Lap is the amount by which each steam port is overlapped by the valve when it is in the mid position. Lead is the amount by which the steam port is open when the piston is at front or back dead centre.

Inside or outside admission refers to whether the steam ports to the cylinder are between the valve heads or on either side of the valve heads. Outside admission is when the ports are at either side of the valve heads, inside being when the ports are between the valve heads. In general practice most modern piston valve locomotives

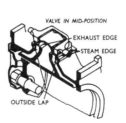
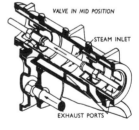

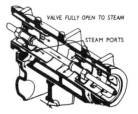

SLIDE VALVE AND STEAM CHEST

PISTON VALVE AND STEAM CHEST

A comparison of the relationships between the slide valve and its steam chest (left) and the piston valve and its operation (right).

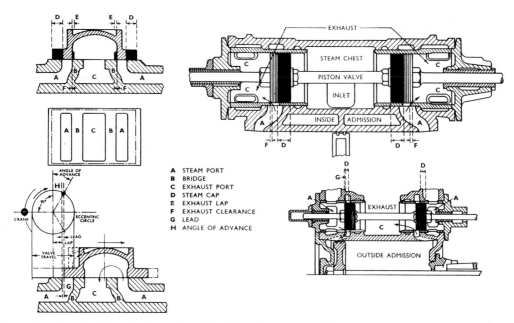

A   STEAM PORT
B   BRIDGE
C   EXHAUST PORT
D   STEAM CAP
E   EXHAUST LAP
F   EXHAUST CLEARANCE
G   LEAD
H   ANGLE OF ADVANCE

Cross-sections through slide and piston valves. The slide valve was an inefficient device compared to the piston valve: the Lancashire and Yorkshire Railway's John Aspinall demonstrated that the power required to move slide valves, due to frictional resistance, was equal to that needed to haul two-and-a-half loaded ten ton wagons. Not surprisingly, the slide valve had been largely displaced by the more efficient piston valve by the turn of the century.

Collett's 4-cylinder designs for the Great Western, such as the Castle class illustrated here, employed inside Walschaerts valve gear with rocking shafts activating the valves of the outside pair of cylinders. The arrangement can be seen here, along with the steampipe leading into the cylinder.

are of the inside admission type, the odd exception being the Bulleid Pacifics and this is mainly due to the unconventional nature of the original design of the valve gear in these locomotives.

There is a third form of valve gear which is unlike either of the two major types referred to above — the rotary cam valve. These were of independent manufacture by companies such as Caprotti and Lentz and were fitted to a variety of classes on a somewhat experimental basis. The major classes to receive this treatment were some of the Stanier and BR Standard Class 5s, the D49 Class 4-4-0 Hunts of the LNER and the BR Class 8P 4-6-2 No. 71000 *Duke of Gloucester*.

The cam-poppet forms of valve gears are more akin to those of the internal combustion engine.

In fairly simple terms, a gearbox on the return crank (affixed to the main driving wheel), drives a rotating, jointed shaft which in turn rotates a cam, which opens and closes the valves. The accompanying diagram shows this in a little more detail.

There are other forms I haven't mentioned, but of these really only the sleeve valve survived in any significant numbers into late nineteenth- and twentieth-century locomotive practice. From memory the only type of locos so fitted, still running in the 1950s and 1960s were some 4-4-2s in use on the Southern Railway. However, even this was a relatively esoteric form of valve gear which would still have to conform to the basic principles already referred to.

Thirty of the 172 Riddles BR Standard Class 5MT 4-6-0s, built from 1956 onwards, were fitted with British Caprotti valve gear, including No 73131, seen here ex-works at Derby. Just one example survives in preservation, No 73129, which is undergoing restoration at the Midland Railway Centre in Derbyshire.

The only currently operational locomotive employing Caprotti valve gear, at least in Britain, is Riddles BR Standard Class 8 Pacific No 71000 *Duke of Gloucester*. This close-up of No 71000 shows, nearest the camera, the return crank gearbox on the centre coupled wheelset and, leading from it, the rear driving shaft. Beyond the anchor link bracket, runs the intermediate driving shaft. The front reversing shaft loads down from the running plate.

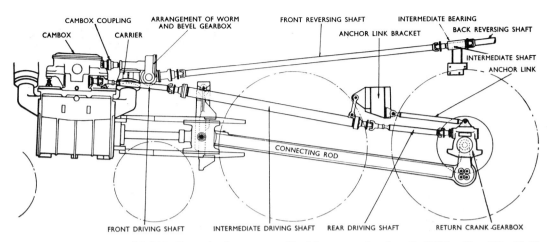

The general arrangement of British Caprotti valve gear, outside drive, as employed on the Riddles Class 8 Pacific No 71000 *Duke of Gloucester* and on the Standard and LMS Class 5MT 4-6-0s fitted with this type of motion.

Returning to our conventional valve gear there are one or two items that we have mentioned which need a little further explanation. The terms lap and lead are frequently bandied about, but what are they? Lap and lead are not unlike the timing in an internal combustion engine, with lap and lead being the equivalent of advance and retard. Alterations can be made to the lap and lead of the valves and in practice, express or mixed traffic designs have lead. Lead means that the steam inlet port is slightly open when the piston reaches front or back dead centre.

The effect of the application of lead is to allow a thin cushion of steam into the clearance space between the piston head and the cylinder cover which is then compressed slightly by the piston as it completes its stroke. This arrangement also helps in creating a freer admission of steam into the cylinder prior to the commencement of the next power stroke — the fresh steam being admitted momentarily before the preceding stroke has finished.

The lap on the valve can be either steam lap or exhaust lap. Lap is the amount by which the valve heads overlap the valve ports with the valve in the mid position. Exhaust lap delays the opening of the exhaust port thus allowing the maximum effort to be gained from each cylinder full of expanding steam. For this reason, exhaust lap is normally associated with goods or shunting locomotives.

In the express or mixed traffic locomotive the very opposite of exhaust lap is what is needed; i.e. the exhaust port needs to be open slightly with the valve in the mid position. The adoption of exhaust clearance, or negative exhaust lap, makes for a freer exhaust with less back pressure. It also means that both sides of the piston are momentarily open to exhaust. In general the amount of exhaust clearance given is about one sixteenth of an inch.

We have now more or less completed our description of those parts of the locomotive which are concerned with making and controlling the driving force — steam. Our next step is to look at how that generated steam is put to productive effort i.e. what happens once that steam is admitted to the cylinder.

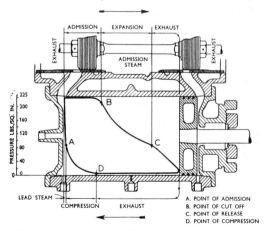

Diagram showing the distribution of steam on one side of the piston for a double stroke.

43

CHAPTER 5

Going Through the Motions

The final shape, size and efficiency of the classic British steam locomotive was a process which covered a great many years, essentially 1804 to 1960. It involved the thoughts, ideas and ambitions of a great many men and at times it produced machines which were works of art as well as superb pieces of mechanical engineering. To be fair it also produced its fair share of monstrosities and not the odd tyrant or three — taken as a whole it was a staggering feat of production and craftsmanship of the highest order.

To arrive at that final design, the BR Standard 9F 2-10-0, we need now to consider how the primal and elementary forces are unleashed in a perfectly controlled fury. How tons of coal and gallons of water have been metamorphosed into

The Riddles BR Standard Class 9F 2-10-0 heavy freight locomotive was the final steam locomotive designed and built for British Railways. It was introduced in 1954 and the last of the total of 251, No 92220 *Evening Star*, was outshopped from Swindon in 1960. The arrangement of Walschaerts gear employed on these locomotives is clearly displayed here by the preserved Crewe-built No 92240. The 9F employed 5ft 0in diameter driving wheels, with the centre wheelset being flangeless.

steam, and how via a series of trap doors, secret passageways, wheels within wheels will be made to turn.

Or, in a less prosaic turn of phrase: how steam is fed from the boiler to the piston and how that makes the wheel go round. We have thus far covered how the steam gets to the piston. In this chapter, we will consider how that steam is turned into horse power at the drawbar.

The modern steam locomotive works on the expansive properties of the steam, but this method of working was some time in coming. The early locomotives worked on admission, with little or no use being made of the expansive properties of the steam. In part the designers didn't fully appreciate, and in some measure they couldn't technologically exploit, this benefit. However, what concerns us is not how steam locomotives came to be expansion engines but how steam is turned into pull on the draw bar and how the back and forth movement of the piston is translated into revolution of the driving wheels.

It should be borne in mind when reading this chapter that we are not concerned with the merits or otherwise of a particular form of motion — this is after all a book produced for the interested layman and enthusiast and is concerned with how the steam locomotive works rather than how much more or less efficient one design was over another. The technical merits or failures of any particular form of motion are in the main beyond the scope of this work. (Motion is the term applied to the collection of rods and levers which, combined together, form the locomotive drive train.)

Many differing forms or types of motion have been tried in British locomotive practice but just two types have dominated, particularly during the twentieth century. These two dominant types are the home-grown Stephenson's link motion and the second like the Belpaire firebox designed by a Belgian engineer, Walschaerts motion.

As a general rule of thumb the Stephenson motion is inside motion, that is, it is located

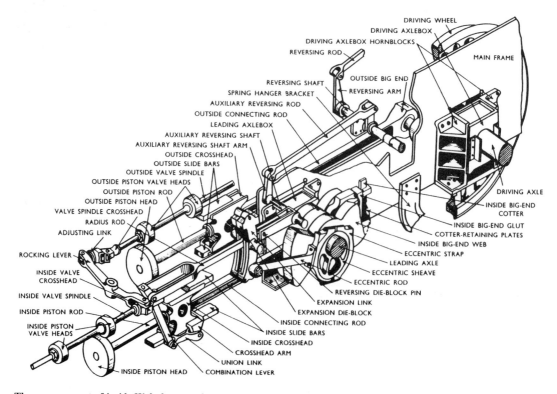

The arrangement of inside Walschaerts valve gear as employed to operate the inside and outside piston valves on Great Western 4-cylinder locomotives, specifically the King and Castle Class 4-6-0s.

Rebuilt Bulleid Southern Railway West Country class 7P5F Pacific No 34027 *Taw Valley* emits a cloud of steam as the cylinder cocks are opened as it moves off shed. It is essential that the cylinders are cleared of any water that may have collected as a result of steam condensing before the locomotive moves.

between the frames with only the connecting and coupling rods immediately visible or in some cases with only the coupling rods visible. In the twentieth century, Stephenson's link motion, with the exception of GWR practice, has tended to be used mainly in freight and shunting locomotives, though as with most things railway there are anomalies. One such surviving oddity is the preserved Stanier Black 5 No. 44767 which is fitted with outside Stephenson link motion.

The GWR, in the main, used a modified form of Stephenson link motion, the major exceptions to this being the Stars, Castles and Kings which were fitted with inside Walschaerts motion, and there was also a class of Hawksworth Panniers built with outside Walschaerts motion.

Throughout the nineteenth century there were a variety of other forms of valve gear, the more noteworthy types being Joy's radial valve gear,

which saw much service on the London and North Western, as did the Allan 'straight link', a modified form of Stephenson's motion. There were other modifications of this type of gear by Ramsbottom on the Lancashire and Yorkshire and another version which was adopted on the GWR. However, before becoming involved in a discussion of the various types and modifications of the motion, some description of the cylinders and piston is desirable.

The cylinder has, in addition to the steam port openings, two other openings. These are for the drain cocks — sometimes referred to as the 'taps'. The purpose of these cocks is to ensure that water, which unlike steam does not compress, can escape from the cylinder. When an engine is standing the drain cocks should always be left open, and often the cylinder cocks are left open when the locomotive is being moved for the first time after a period at rest, such as on setting off from a station or siding. The reason for doing so is not to frighten the kids or make super photographs, but to dispel any water which may have gathered as the result of steam condensing in the steam chest or cylinder.

In the event of the locomotive 'priming' whilst in motion the 'cocks' are opened to expel the water carried into the piston. If they are not, the result can be the destruction of the cylinder covers or piston head or damage to the cylinder block. The motion itself can be bent or distorted, as we have already mentioned in Chapter Two. There is a third drain cock which drains any condensed water from the steam chest.

The previous chapter described how steam was admitted to the cylinders via the steam chest, which is cast integrally with the cylinder block, and how the valves, located in the steam chest, determined whether steam was admitted in front of, or behind, the piston in the cylinder. The valves also determine for what proportion of the stroke of the piston steam is admitted to the cylinders. The duration of the opening — the 'cut-off' — is regulated via the reversing lever situated in the cab in front of the driver.

To ensure the valves open and close at the right time, and in the correct sequence, there are a series of rods and levers connected to the reversing lever and it is here that the first major difference between the Stephenson and the Walschaerts motion is to be found. The Stephenson motion uses two eccentrics, one to achieve forward motion the other for backward movement. The Walschaerts motion has only one eccentric.

The inside cylinder block from a Great Western 4-cylinder locomotive, in this case Collett King Class 8P 4-6-0 No 6023 *King Edward II*, subject of a restoration at Didcot Railway Centre.

(The two diagrams show the different arrangements of rods and eccentrics of the Walschaerts and Stephenson types of motion.)

The eccentric rod or rods are a part of a crank. Their function is to turn the rotary movement of the wheel into the back and forth, reciprocating, movement needed to operate the valves. The eccentric rod achieves this action by virtue of being offset from the wheel or axle centre. Thus,

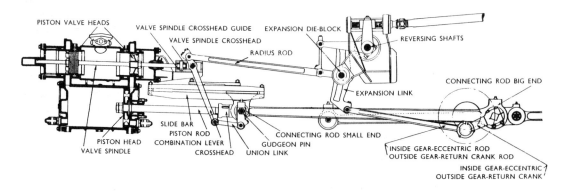

The basic arrangement of the components of the Walschaerts valve gear, which takes its name from its Belgian inventor.

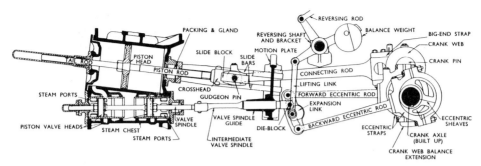

Arrangement of the Stephenson link valve gear with outside admission piston valves and direct motion. Stephenson gear was employed in the majority of inside-cylinder locomotives built for Britain's railways and, with some significant exceptions, on all the locomotives built for the Great Western Railway.

as the wheel rotates, the eccentric describes a circle offset from the axle or wheel centre. The effect of this is that as the wheel turns, the offset is at one point nearer to the front end of the steam chest or cylinder and as the wheel continues its revolution the offset moves with it thus moving farther away from the front or back as the case may be. The wheel turns by degrees, the offset moves closer to or farther away from the front of the locomotive and so produces a back and forth movement on the eccentric rod and hence upon the valves.

The way in which the eccentricity of the eccentric is achieved differs between the Walschaerts and Stephenson motion. In the Walschaerts type the offset is achieved by the use of a return crank on the driving axle. In the Stephenson type this same effect is achieved through the use of a built-up lobe on the crank axle and by the way in which the eccentric sheaves are constructed (see diagram). The methods may differ but the net effect is the same.

The reversing rod from the cab is connected through a lifting link to the expansion link, which is itself attached to the eccentric rod. The other end of this is attached to the return crank (in the case of the Walschaerts motion) or to the crank axle in the case of the Stephenson type.

In the Stephenson gear the expansion link is connected to the valve spindle via an intermediate valve spindle, a sort of bolt-on bit extending the valve spindle itself. In the Walschaerts system the expansion link is connected to the valve spindle through a radius rod — though the actual connection between valve spindle and radius rod is made via the combination lever, also known as

the 'pendulum link' because it swings back and forth like the pendulum of a clock. This lever is attached to the radius rod, to the valve spindle and also to the union link. This last is also attached to, and moves with, the crosshead.

The reversing rod controlled by the driver acts on the expansion link, either by raising or lowering the position of the die block within it, and through this the driver is able to determine the degree of cut-off and whether the locomotive will move forwards or backwards. In the Walschaerts system the movement of the radius rod is controlled by the expansion link, which in turn acts upon the valve rod. In the Stephenson link type the intermediate valve spindle is controlled directly from the expansion link.

What is happening here is that as the die block is moved within the expansion link it alters the actual distance which the valve rod moves, shortening or lengthening, increasing or decreasing the cut-off, or reversing the direction of travel from fore gear to back gear. This is determined by which side of the piston head steam is admitted to and in the case of the cut-off, for how much of the stroke of the piston the admission port remains open.

In the Stephenson system the lowering of the die block in the expansion link aligns the valve rod with the forward eccentric. Conversely raising the expansion link die block aligns the backward eccentric with the valve rod and the degree of raising or lowering determines cut-off. This system is sometimes referred to as direct motion.

These are the levers and rods which determine the direction of travel and the duration of steam admission to the cylinders. Or to put it another way, they are the means by which the valve events are determined. However, these rods, links and levers are only a part of the motion.

There is another area concerning valve gear which might benefit from some further explanation and this is the way in which the valves are operated in three and four cylinder locomotives, where the additional cylinders are mounted between the frames. In locomotives with three or more cylinders the actuating mechanism for the valves of the inside cylinders is often derived from the operation of the valves on the outside cylinders, thus removing the need for extra sets of valve gear between the frames. This particular area of locomotive engineering practice has been the centre of a great deal of controversy and has suffered more than its share of troubles.

Perhaps the most well known and widely discussed of these problems are those relating to the Gresley three cylinder locomotives, which have, rightly or wrongly, gained something of a

reputation for the overheating and damage to their inside big ends. Opinion is that the problem is caused by the wear on the derived motion for the inside valves.

On Gresley's three cylinder locomotives the actuating method for the valve events of the inside cylinder was derived through a set of rocking levers operated via the valve spindles of the external motion. These levers would, in time, wear down the fulcrum pins around which they were located, with the result that the excess play became translated into a longer cut-off on the middle valve.

This wearing down of the fulcrum pins, allowed increased movement — cut-off — on the inside valve, creating a situation in which the inside cylinder and motion was doing a greater proportion of the work than the outer cylinders with the result that it ran hot. This problem led directly to the incorporation of one of surely the oddest of warning devices: enginemen were warned of overheating in the middle big end by

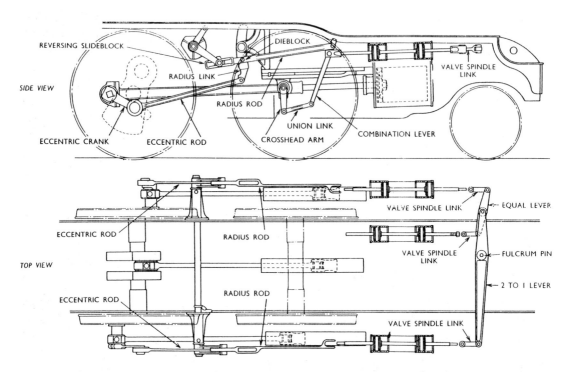

The 3-cylinder locomotives designed by Sir Nigel Gresley for the London and North Eastern Railway saw a further variant on the use of Walschaerts gear, this time employing an ingenious system of conjugated levers to operate the valve gear of the middle cylinder. The original idea belonged to H. Holcroft and was refined by Gresley. The valves of the inside cylinder are activated by a 'two-to-one' lever working off the extended valve spindles of the outside cylinders.

the smell of garlic! Puts a whole new meaning on 'what's cooking?'!

Finally we come to the most unusual form of valve operation used in British locomotive practice, the Bulleid chain-driven valve gear. Bulleid studied under Gresley and was acutely aware of the problems of the valve train and the derived motion associated with three cylinder engines. Bulleid's solution to the problems was both novel and controversial: the motion for all three valves was enclosed in an oil bath/sump and driven by chain gears. However, the valves themselves were the conventional piston valves.

Bulleid, like so many locomotive engineers before him, was an innovator and his West Country and Merchant Navy Class locomotives were choc-a-bloc with the most innovative features of the day. The only difficulty with this sort of approach is that sometimes the available technology isn't up to the applications it is asked to do or, as in Bulleid's case, old technology will not withstand the new applications.

Bulleid may have removed the problem of overheated middle big ends, but he succeeded only in creating another hot spot. The sump couldn't be kept oiltight with the result that oil escaped everywhere and would ignite, occasionally with highly undesirable results. While researching another project I spoke to men responsible for maintaining and operating un-rebuilt Bulleid Pacifics in preservation and discovered that, with the use of new modern-day jointing and packing materials, sump leakage has virtually been eliminated. The packing/jointing material used by Bulleid was leather, so I am informed.

The previous paragraphs covered the operating mechanism for the valves and the valve timing, the following cover what might be described as the power train. The motion parts in this series of connections are; the piston head which is bolted to the piston rod, which in turn is fastened to the crosshead, as is the connecting rod and this rod provides the drive to the main driving wheel

Another variant on the Walschaerts motion, as employed by the Southern Railway's Richard Maunsell in his U class Moguls, which were fitted with 6ft 0in coupled wheels.

Close-up of the Walschaerts valve gear on a Stanier LMS Princess Coronation Class 8P 4-6-2. At the top can be seen the valve spindle with its connection to the valve spindle crosshead guide and the valve spindle crosshead. Just entering the picture on the left is the radius rod. Below, the piston rod sits squarely between the slide bar, attached to the crosshead. The horizontal union link connects with the vertical combination lever which mates with the valve spindle crosshead.

— this is the means by which the motive force of the steam pressure acting upon the cylinder head is imparted to the locomotive.

The piston rod enters the cylinder through the rear cylinder cover which incorporates a steam-tight gland. This gland is easily accessed and the packing within it changed thus, at least in theory, ensuring a steamtight fit of the piston rod as it enters the cylinder. A similar arrangement is used to ensure the valve rod is likewise steam-tight as it enters the steam chest.

At the opposite end from the piston head the piston rod is attached to the crosshead and is secured in place on the crosshead by use of a cotter pin. The connecting rod is also attached to the crosshead and is secured into the crosshead by means of a gudgeon pin which is effectively the little end. The crosshead itself is supported by the slide bars, which may take the form to be seen in the diagram, or it may be that the cross-head sits between two more widely spaced slide bars, rather than in the slung-beneath fashion of the diagram.

The slide bars are to prevent the oblique thrust of the connecting rod from bending the piston rod and, depending on which side of the piston power is being applied, the corresponding opposite side of the slide bar takes the strain. One of the most difficult tasks in the restoration of a preserved locomotive is ensuring the correct alignment of the slide bars — the re-metalling of the white metal bearing faces of the crosshead is another tricky little task.

Just as in the case of the eccentric, the connecting rod is also on a crank, i.e. it is located off-centre in relation to the centre line of the driving axle. It is this use of cranks which turns reciprocating movement into rotary motion, or

Piston rod, slide bars and crosshead of a Great Western King Class 4-6-0. The relative simplicity of this arrangement compared to other designs using Walschaerts gear is explained by the fact that the gear was located between the frames with the operation of the valves of the outside cylinders through an arrangement of rocking levers.

conversely turns the back and forth movement of the piston into the revolving of the wheel. The location of the connecting rod on the crosshead is known as the little end and its location on the driving axle as the big end.

The Stephenson and Walschaerts motions may have ended up as the major ones of their type, but to arrive at this eventual two-horse race a lot of other runners dropped by the wayside. Some of the also-rans were singularly unsuccessful, others were not. One or two examples of what might be described as non-standard arrangements are still running today and so including a mention of some of the more long-lived varieties might be useful.

One of the motions that was not, in its day, an also-ran and is still in use today is the radial valve gear of David Joy. Joy's gear is in use today in locomotives such as the ex-LNER Y7s on the Great Central and Middleton Railways and, in view of the gear's major antecedants, it is equally fitting that some of the surviving examples are in former London North Western and Lancashire and Yorkshire engines, such as the ex-LNWR 0-8-0 Super D No 9395, the ex-L & Y Radial Tank No 1008, and ex-L & Y 3F 0-6-0 No 1300, at present in working order at Steamtown Carnforth.

David Joy began his career with the famous locomotive building company of E. B. Wilson of Leeds and played a leading role in the development of the Jenny Lind 2-2-2. He went on to become locomotive superintendent of the Oxford, Worcester and Wolverhampton Railway. While it is true that Joy's motion removed the need for the use of eccentrics it did have some shortcomings, particularly as it involved the use of a hole in the connecting rod — a fact which in service tended to weaken or put undue strain on the rod. This was probably the major reason why the Joy gear was never taken up for use in major express designs.

However, the Joy valve gear was adopted by London and North Western Railway and was used almost exclusively on inside cylinder locomotives, built at Crewe between 1880 and 1923. The major difference between the Joy system and that of the Walschaerts and Stephenson versions is, as I've already mentioned, that

the Joy type does not use an eccentric for determining the valve events.

The relationship between the motion parts in the steam locomotive is to an extent analogous with that to be found in the internal combustion engine, the difference being that in the internal combustion engine the movement is usually in the vertical rather than the horizontal plane (though initially many locomotives too had vertical cylinders and the Sentinel-type engines such as the one at the Middleton Railway, in Leeds, or those at the Buckinghamshire Railway Centre still do).

The remaining items of the motion jigsaw are the coupling rods. These rods connect the driving wheels to the main driving wheel, i.e. the one which is driven by the connecting rod. The number of coupling rods varies with the number of driving wheels. Thus a 4-4-0 has one coupling rod per side, a 4-6-0 has two and so on. The use of multi-coupled wheels gives extra adhesion and a more even transmission of power, thus reducing the propensity to slipping, or wheel spin.

There are one or two other variations to the basic motion which are worthy of some explanation. In essence these items concern alterations to the Walschaerts-type motion to derive the valve events for locomotives with more than two cylinders, particularly the three cylinder locomotives designed for the LNER by Sir Nigel Gresley. The other area in which different rods and links were used was in the compound type of locomotive. I shall deal first with the problem of obtaining valve events for multi-cylindered locomotives where the valve movement for the inside cylinder(s) is derived from the external valve events.

To obtain the valve events for the inside cylinder without using another set of valve gear, expansion links, eccentrics, radius rods and the like, Gresley, in association with Holcroft, designed a linkage which eliminated the need for the third set of valve gear for the inside cylinder — the two-to-one lever.

This lever is driven by extending forward the valve spindles from the two outside cylinders to a lever set at right angles to them. The movement of the extended valve spindles from the outside cylinders operates through the two-to-one link to

Introduced in 1935, the Stanier 8F 2-8-0 was designed to update the LMS's fleet of heavy freight locomotives. It was also later built in quantities for the War Department and saw service in North Africa and the Middle East. The 8F incorporated many design tenets laid down by Churchward on the Great Western thirty years earlier and which Stanier, who joined the LMS from Swindon, faithfully adhered to, such as the use of a taper boiler with Belpaire firebox. He did, however, opt for outside Walschaerts valve gear as opposed to the Stephenson motion employed by Churchward, one of the reasons being its greater ease of maintenance. Interestingly, No 48431 is one of the 8Fs built at Swindon, under government order, in 1944. It now works on the Keighley and Worth Valley Railway in West Yorkshire.

This angle on Standard Class 9F 2-10-0 No 92220 *Evening Star*, the last steam locomotive built for British Railways (in 1960, and another Swindon product) illustrates its use of the wide firebox. On the top of the firebox is the steam manifold, supplying steam to power various cab controls, while below the cab side can be seen the injectors and associated pipework. It is the fireman's job to operate these.

Fireboxes in the raw, all of the Belpaire type, whose square shape increased the water space around the firebox. All three copper fireboxes here are from ex-GWR locomotives under restoration in the workshops of Birmingham Railway Museum in August 1991: 2800 Class 2-8-0s Nos 3803 (left) and 2807 (right) and 4900 Hall Class 4-6-0 No 4983 *Albert Hall* (centre).

A glimpse inside the smokebox of Peppercorn LNER A2 Class 8P7F 4-6-2 No 60532 *Blue Peter*. Clearly seen is the Kylchap double blastpipe, a device invented by the Finnish designer, Kyala, in collaboration with the legendary French locomotive engineer, André Chapelon, and first employed on the LNER by Sir Nigel Gresley. *Blue Peter* is seen in the final stages of its overhaul by the North Eastern Locomotive Preservation Group in its workshop at ICI Wilton on Teeside. The locomotive is now a regular performer on the main line.

After withdrawal, rebuilt Bulleid Merchant Navy Class 8P Pacific No 35029 *Ellerman Lines* was acquired by the National Railway Museum and used as a 'cutaway' exhibit to show the workings of the steam locomotive, which it does most effectively. Clearly seen here are the steampipes of the cylinders, the superheater header, the differing diameters of the large and small tubes, the construction of the wide firebox and its staying. No 35029 is currently on display at York, with push-button electric motors showing the operation of the valve gear and motion.

A typical Great Western profile, as exhibited by Churchward 4500 Class 4MT 2-6-2T No 5572, a resident of Didcot Railway Centre. Note the Belpaire firebox — and the whistle! — taper boiler, safety valve bonnet and slope to the front of the sidetanks, to improve forward visibility from the cab.

Sunlight creates a *chiarascuro* effect inside the rusting smokebox of Churchward/Collett 2884 Class 8F 2-8-0 No 3803, under restoration at the Birmingham Railway Museum. The orifices for chimney and steampipe are visible, as is the front tubeplate.

Arguably the least appealing side of steam is the disposal of its waste products, although the crewman here is taking suitable precautions as he disposes of the 'char' from the smokebox of Collett Great Western King Class 8P 4-6-0 No 6024 *King Edward I* on the coal stage road at Didcot Railway Centre. Visible inside the smokebox is the double blastpipe, while behind the falling ash can be seen the cylinder covers of the two inside cylinders.

The injectors and associated pipework of BR Standard Class 4MT 2-6-0 No 76079, nominally based on the East Lancashire Railway. Via a clever system of cones, the injectors control the supply of water to the boiler.

Over the period of its construction, the Stanier LMS Class 5MT 4-6-0 became the subject of a number of experimental variations, a quantity for example being fitted with British Caprotti rotary cam valve gear. Just one locomotive, however, received outside Stephenson link valve gear, No 44767, and it survives to this day, now named, appropriately, *George Stephenson*. Nominally based on the North Yorkshire Moors Railway, No 44767 is passed for main-line running and is expected to work in both Wales and Scotland during 1993. Refer to the diagram on page 49 for the key to the various motion parts seen here.

Outside Walschaerts motion was selected by the design team headed by Robert Riddles for all twelve Standard designs, largely following LMS practice as laid down by Stanier. Displaying the arrangement of links, levers and cranks is Class 7P6F Pacific No 70000 *Britannia*. For a key to the elements of the Walschaerts system, see the diagram on page 48.

Inside motion was employed on the majority of smaller locomotives built for Britain's railways, before the advent of the Standard designs. This was especially true of the ubiquitous six-coupled goods and tank locomotives – far and away the most numerous British wheel arrangement. The Stephenson gear seen here, with its complexity of rods, cranks, eccentrics and shafts, belongs to Maunsell Southern Railway Q Class 4F 0-6-0 No 541, a class introduced as late as 1938.

actuate the valve movements of the inside cylinder.

This appears to be a fairly simple solution to the problem of the valve train for the inside cylinder. However, in practice the design proved problematic and on occasions the inside cylinder was doing more than its fair share of the work. The difficulties were caused by the wearing of the fulcrum pins (see diagram). These pins wear, and when they do the effect is to increase the degree of cut-off on the inside valve. This puts increased effort on the inside cylinder and motion and the middle big end is the part which bears the brunt of that strain.

The problem was partially solved by the use of hardened pins, but it was never entirely eliminated. This particular form of motion is sometimes referred to as either conjugated valve gear or derived motion, i.e. it is derived from the valve events of the outside cylinders.

Oliver Bulleid was a pupil under Gresley and in the early years of Bulleid's career he was well aware of the problems of Gresley's solution to the inside motion problem. This knowledge was behind Bulleid's thinking when he designed the chain-driven valve gear for his own Pacifics. In this system, cranks and eccentrics are eschewed in favour of a chain drive from the main axle through a three throw jockey shaft — see diagram. However, the end result is still that a series of levers open and close the steam ports in the steam chest to admit steam to the cylinders at the correct moment and similarly to exhaust.

In addition to the Gresley, Bulleid and Joy variations there is another area worthy of a mention, that of compounding. Compounding was concerned with trying to gain maximum expansion from the available steam and a number of systems were developed. The main contenders were the Webb, Smith, De Glehn and Worsdell-von Borries systems. The Webb system had two high pressure cylinders feeding one low pressure cylinder, whereas Smith's had the opposite. De Glehn had two of each and the Worsdell-von Borries had just one of each.

The use of compounding has over the years been something of a cause célébre and arguments and differences of opinions have never been entirely silenced. One of the most famous of compound type locomotives, the Midland 4-4-0s

of 1902, which used Smith's system of one high and two low pressure cylinders, was saved for the national collection and is perhaps the best testament to the importance attached to the use of compounding as a technical innovation.

The choices of the number of cylinders and whether there should be more low pressure or high pressure cylinders formed one part of the equation; stroke, bore, and ratios formed another. In practical terms the Webb type compounds of the LNWR had something of a reputation for being difficult to get started. This has been attributed to the small size of the high pressure cylinders — on the other hand the Midland compounds have a reputation for high speed running, turning in 90mph plus on the Leeds to Carlisle route.

First introduced in 1902 the Midland Compounds were still being built after the grouping of 1923. However, in British locomotive practice the use of compounding ceased in about 1930, the cause being attributed to improvements in the valve gear. Improvements in the valve timing meant that there was little to be gained from the re-use of exhaust steam — the disadvantages outweighed the expansionary efficiency gains.

The compound locomotive, just like its simple sister, has the need for a set of motion to provide the timing for the valve sequences and to provide a source of motive power to the wheel with the added complication of timing the exhaust stroke of the high pressure cylinder(s) to the admission stroke of the secondary or low pressure cylinder(s). To put it another way, in the compound engine the low pressure cylinder was part of the high pressure cylinder exhaust system and could, if incorrectly timed or unduly restricted, cause excessive back pressure which would in turn restrict the free running of the locomotive.

The use of compounding necessitated the incorporation of various means to overcome the problems of getting steam into the low pressure cylinder, direct from the boiler, to aid in starting the train and in relieving back pressure on the exhaust from the high pressure cylinder(s). To overcome the former, starting valves were used. Sometimes these were of the automatic type and sometimes they were non-automatic types operated by the driver. To solve the latter problem various

Mechanical lubricators mounted on the running plate of a rebuilt Bulleid Southern Railway Merchant Navy Class Pacific. Note the feed pipes.

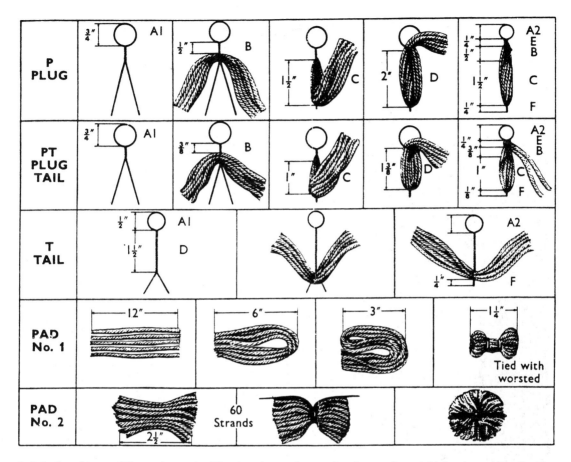

Lubrication of many of the moving parts of the steam locomotive requires the use of worsted trimmings which allow the even distribution of oil, either allowing it to be siphoned off or by acting as 'restrictors' to the flow. This diagram shows how the various types of trimming were prepared.

types of pressure relief valves were used.

An interesting feature of the compounding era was that in a perverse way it prolonged the life of the single driver, as many compounds were built with the high pressure cylinder(s) driving one set of drivers whilst the low pressure cylinder(s) drove the other. With hindsight it seems that much time and energy was expended on compounding with less than adequate savings in return.

The motion, pistons, valves, rods, levers and links all rely on bearings of one sort or another. The most widely used forms of bearing are bronze bushes with white metal bearing surfaces. However, towards the end of the steam locomotive building era, roller or needle bearings came into use. All these moving parts had to be lubricated and a variety of means were used to do this.

To lubricate the cylinders and valves the two most widely used systems are the mechanical lubricator, or the cab-mounted hydrostatic sight-feed lubricator. The mechanical lubricator is generally mounted on the running plate and is actuated via a lever from the motion, which in turn operates a ratchet wheel. This turns a cam inside the lubricator body and the cam operates a pump which force-feeds oil to the cylinders, valves and, in some cases, axleboxes.

The hydrostatic lubricator works on a displacement principle: exhaust steam forces oil from a reservoir into the oil pipes where steam carries it to a choke close to the main steam pipe. Here it enters the cylinder via the steam chest. This is atomised oil, a fine suspension of oil droplets in steam, and is carried into the steam chest and cylinders with the steam which drives the locomotive. The oil used in this part of the lubrication is of a different type than is used in the other areas, due to it being required to withstand not only high pressure but also high temperature. A superheated steam locomotive uses yet another different oil in its lubrication from that used in saturated steam engines because of the temperature differences.

Lubrication of the other moving parts takes numerous forms: by hand, by siphon, by restrictor plug and by fountain. These types of lubrication use worsted trimmings (see diagram). Each of these methods of lubrication are utilised in different parts of the locomotive and tender, if fitted.

Because of the importance of lubrication I will give a resumé of where the differing types of oil-feed system are employed, beginning with the 'pad' type. This is used primarily in the under-keeps of the axleboxes. The pad is kept supplied with oil from a tail, which siphons oil from the oil bath in the underkeep.

The restrictor plug method is employed in the oiling of the big ends and coupling rods. The restrictor is generally a trimming made as in the diagram, but sometimes a needle or metal restrictor plug is used. Oil is fed to the restrictor by the movement imparted to the oil as the rods move round with the motion of the locomotive.

From the restrictor plug, oil runs down to a felt pad in the bearing.

The siphon method is used to oil parts such as the slide bars, axleboxes and horn cheeks. Once again this is a worsted trimming, but unlike the plug type the siphon trimming is of the tail type, where oil is drawn up through the tail and then allowed to drip down from there onto the part requiring lubrication.

One anomaly in the lubrication stakes is our old friend Oliver Bulleid again: the entire valve gear drive is contained in an oil-filled sump, just as with the internal combustion engine. Another is the fountain-type lubricator, which was used to lubricate axleboxes on a few classes of locomotive.

Some of the smaller bearings and locomotives fitted with roller bearings used grease in place of oil for lubrication. The interesting point about this is that if oil was required the driver was responsible, if it was a greased bearing it was the fitter's responsibility, a practice which is still maintained today at some railways.

We have now covered the parts which make up the motion, the means by which they are kept lubricated and this seems to be a good point at which to conclude this chapter. The next one will cover the frames, wheels, axles, pony trucks, and the rest of the bits and pieces which form the rolling chassis on which the whole locomotive sits.

CHAPTER 6

And Round Went The Wheel

The previous chapters have taken us from the raising of steam in the boiler to the transmission of that power through the pistons, cylinders and motion — this one will look at how all these parts come together and are supported in performing the ultimate task of moving goods or passenger trains through the land.

The rolling chassis of the locomotive consists of wheels, axles and their boxes, supporting a set of frames on which the cab, footplate, running plate and the power plant of boiler/firebox sits. There are other items which make up the locomotive chassis; stretchers, braces, drag boxes, horn guides and the like all come together to provide the ultimate mobile power plant.

These basic categories can be further sub-

Wheels galore! A wealth of driving and bogie wheelsets parked along one of the roads at Didcot Railway Centre in Oxfordshire. In the foreground are the driving wheels for Great Western 7200 Class 2-8-2T No 7202 which is currently under restoration at Didcot. As befits a heavy freight locomotive (the class was much employed on iron ore and coal traffic) where adhesion and power take priority over speed, the coupled wheels are of just 4ft 7½in diameter.

divided. Wheels can be of the driving, trailing or leading variety, frames can be of the bar, inside or outside variety; and axleboxes too can be of various designs depending on which axles they are supporting.

The way into a description of the rolling chassis is probably to begin with the wheels and work up, so to speak. The wheel arrangement of a locomotive varies in relation to the duties for which it was built, the loading gauge of the routes it will work along and the weights of the loads it will be expected to haul. But before embarking on this, a few words on the development of the frame and the structure of the rolling chassis.

The development of the locomotive frame spans several decades and a plethora of differing modes of construction. In some of the very earliest constructions it was the boiler and firebox assembly which provided the rigid strength of the locomotive, in others wooden frames bore the brunt of the active forces. There was also the sandwich frame which utilised both wood and iron, the iron plates being the bread and the wood the filling.

Not all early locomotives used springs and the design and placing of the axleboxes was another area where only trial and error brought about a satisfactory system. It is very easy with hindsight and the benefits of modern techniques and technologies to see where the early pioneers were in error. That they overcame the difficulties and produced such elegant yet robust machines is no small tribute to the ingenuity of these men, in an age without computer-aided design, positive feedback systems or any of the other myriad inventions and data available to today's engineers.

As engineers began to comprehend the nature of the forces at work in and on the locomotive, so the designs and methods of construction began to alter. One small but significant change was to leave the boiler mounted on a slide arrangement at the firebox end and only fully secured at the smokebox end. Other changes to the frame came not through design innovation per se but through improvements in steel and iron making. The ability to make large and less brittle plates of steel altered the way cylinders were mounted and the design of axleboxes and horn guides.

The development of the modern, slotted, plate steel frame was accompanied by similar improvements to the wheels, axles, bearings, and other chassis fittings as locomotives grew in size, weight and complexity. However, it is worth remembering that it was not only railway technology that was improving during this period but also many other areas of industry, and it was changes in these spheres which could and did help to alter railway practice.

To return to our narrative, the most common of all wheel arrangements is the 0-6-0. This configuration is used in both tank or tender locomotive designs and is generally associated with freight and shunting locomotives. In general terms the 0-6-0 arrangement has wheel diameters in the three foot to five foot range and is a design for power rather than speed. However, there are many wheel arrangements from 2-2-2 through 2-4-0, 2-6-0, 2-8-0, 4-6-0, 4-6-2 *et al.*

The single driver, the 2-2-2 arrangement, was in use on express locomotives into the early years of the twentieth century, but in the main, most post-nineteenth century passenger locomotives have had four, six, or on occasions eight coupled wheels. In the passenger locomotive the wheel diameter has tended to be between six feet two inches and seven feet. Mixed traffic designs have tended to be between four feet eight inches and six feet two inches.

Why so many wheel arrangements and so many different diameters? The answer is related to three criteria; one is the weight carried by each wheel/axle, another is the speed at which the locomotive is intended to work; then there is the load it is expected to haul. Each of these ingredients plays a part in determining the number and diameter of the wheels.

A locomotive does not have a gearbox as such, only the means to admit steam to the cylinder for longer or shorter periods. Hence wheel diameter plays a part in the relationship between piston speed and the maximum revolutions per minute of the driving wheel in a way it does not in a vehicle with a geared drive. The rpm at the wheel of a gear-driven vehicle is altered or amended via the use of the gears, which alter the relationship between piston speed and the miles per hour velocity of the vehicle. (This relationship is

Following the example of Churchward's 2800 class, eventually most of the major coal- and minerals-carrying railways had fleets of locomotives of the 2-8-0 wheel arrangement, the eight coupled wheels offering the necessary adhesion and the leading pony truck the opportunity to use a large boiler, as well as its usual function as a guiding wheelset. The 02 class 2-8-0 was introduced by Sir Nigel Gresley on to the Great Northern Railway in 1921 and subsequently refined by him during his time with the LNER. The 02/4 was the final development, introduced in 1943 with the Type 100A boiler. One of the class, No 63945, stands in the yard of its home shed of Retford (36E).

usually expressed as a set of ratios.) In a steam locomotive the piston speed and wheel rpm are related to each other directly — there are no intervening gears to alter or amend the ratio.

There is, naturally, the obligatory exception to this in British steam locomotive practice, the building of a steam turbine locomotive. Here the drive was through gears from the turbine to the front driving wheel and through the normal coupling rods to the others. However, the gearing of the turbine locomotive was reduction gearing and was to step down the turbine speed not alter the final drive ratio.

The 'Turbomotive' as this engine was known,

was a modified, Stanier Princess Royal Class Pacific, numbered in LMS stock as 6202. It was converted back to the Walschaerts motion used on all the other locomotives of the class in 1952 after seventeen years in service as a steam turbine locomotive.

The size of the wheel in a locomotive type or wheel arrangement is, as I've already stated, very relevant to the job the locomotive is designed to do and the position of the wheel relative to that end. Driving wheels are of larger diameter than bogie wheels and passenger locomotive driving wheel diameters are greater than those of freight engines because they allow a higher miles per

A typical example of the suburban passenger tank, Alfred Hill's N7 Class 3MT 0-6-2T introduced on to the Great Eastern Railway's north-east London services in 1914. These locomotives, which were expected to show a fair turn of speed in between the large number of stops on the lines to Enfield Town, Chingford and Hertford, were fitted with 4ft 10in driving wheels. The sole survivor of the N7s, No 69621 A. J. Hill is seen at its birthplace of Stratford in March 1991.

hour speed per foot travel of piston. Indeed the driving wheel size is usually derived from the equation of optimum piston speed and the intended operational maximum speed for the locomotive.

The addition of wheels in front of or behind the driving wheels, as in the arrangements 2-4-2, 2-6-2, 4-6-2, etc. are for two main reasons: improved stability at speed, and weight distribution, though there are other factors relating to matters such as the length of the wheel base and the radii of the curves on the routes the locomotive is designed to work over. These wheels play no part in the locomotion process, so their diameter has no bearing on the performance capabilities of the locomotive other than those associated with improvements in stability or weight distribution.

The increasing number of driving wheels, used as locomotives became larger, heavier, more powerful and faster, was related not only to weight distribution but also to the locomotive's pulling power. The use of multiple coupled wheels gives increased adhesion and thus allows heavier trains and reduces the propensity to slipping.

The benefits of the coupled wheel were early discoveries and the real giants of the steam era were those engines with many coupled wheels, such as the articulated twelve-coupled Garratts and the ten-coupled engines such as the Decapod, the Lickey Banker and the much loved Riddles 9Fs. In British practice, ten was big and six or eight the more likely combination. However, in Southern Africa and in the Americas ten-coupled wheels could quite easily become sixteen or more.

Thus the wheels are more than simply that which the locomotive rolls along on — they spread the weight, increase pulling power, help with stability and in part determine the types of duties for which the locomotive is suited. The wheels themselves are cast and are then fitted with changeable (i.e. removable) steel tyres and, where applicable, balance weights. The major part of the fastening of tyre to rim is achieved through the shrink fit method. However, this is not the only means of fastening; there is also a device known as a Gibson ring which holds the tyre to the rim of the cast wheel centre. The

Gibson ring is essentially a lipped insert in the outer edge of the wheel casting with corresponding grips on the tyre.

In the main wheels are of the spoked variety, though our old friend Mr. Bulleid patented a wheel in conjunction with the steelmakers Firth Brown & Co. The BFB (Bulleid/Firth Brown) wheel, which was some ten percent lighter than the spoked variety, was fitted to the Bulleid Pacifics and to the Q1 0-6-0s built by Bulleid for the Southern during the mid-years of the Second World War. This wheel did not use the Gibson ring method of fixing tyre to rim, instead just a simple lipped edge was used though, of course, the shrink fit was still retained.

The replaceable flanged tyres are, or can be, turned to specific dimensions to suit the routes over which the locomotive works and different wheels within any configuration can have differing tyre profiles. The tyre is shrink-fitted to the wheel casting and will be 'turned' or re-profiled several times during its working life and a wheel may have a multitude of new tyres.

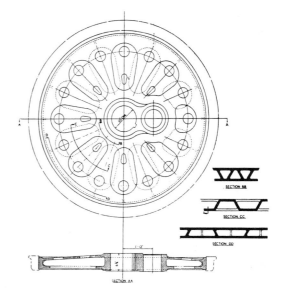

Pattern and cross-section of the Bulleid-Firth-Brown wheel. The Southern Railway's Oliver Bulleid collaborated with the Sheffield-based steelmakers, Firth Brown, in developing this new type of wheel, which took its inspiration from the American 'boxpok' design. The wheel proved stronger than the conventional spoked type, yet was ten per cent lighter. It was employed on Bulleid's Pacifics and on his Q1 0-6-0 freight locomotive.

The Stanier 8F heavy freight locomotive employed eight coupled wheels of 4ft 8½in diameter. Introduced on to the LMS in 1935, the type was subsequently built by all the 'big four' railways, having been selected as the 'standard' War Department locomotive, until the advent of its simpler and cheaper cousin, the Austerity 2-8-0. Eventually, 666 8Fs saw service with British Railways, a handful becoming the last working steam locomotives on BR in August 1968.

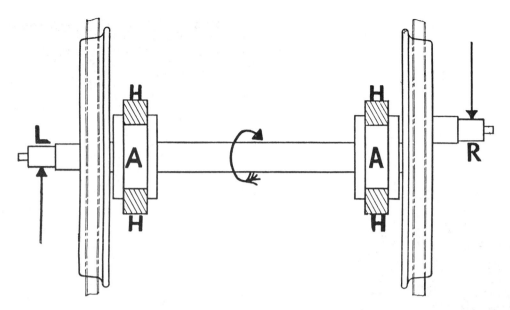

The driving wheel, viewed from above, with wedges at the back of the axleboxes (A) and horn checks (H) without wedges at the front of the axleboxes.

The wheels are press-fitted to the axles before being drilled for the fitting of the crank or coupling rod pins. When this has been done the wheels are then balanced — in much the same way as the wheels of a motor car are balanced and for the same reasons.

The axle immediately behind each wheel is buffed and polished to create a journal around which the axlebox sits, supporting the frame and all the rest of the locomotive. In the case of locomotives with inside cylinders or those with more than two cylinders there is a crank axle. In general this axle is made up of three sections which form the central axis and at their outer extremities are attached to the wheels. Between these three sections are the balance weights, or webs, and the connecting rod cranks and journals.

The axlebox is fitted over the journal polished into the axle and it is located in the frame by the horns and horn ties which are bolted or rivetted to the cut-out in the frame. Below the axlebox and its supporting horn tie is the spring. The springs are generally of the tempered steel leaf type on the driving wheels but may be of coil or helical type on bogies or any of a variety of pony or trailing trucks.

The springing is secured to the mainframe through plates rivetted to the frames which carry

An express passenger locomotive driving wheel, this being the central 6ft 8½in diameter wheelset of Collett GWR Castle Class 7P 4-6-0 No 5080 *Defiant*. This angle also reveals the mainframe of the locomotive and the springing. Note the balance weight incorporated into the driving wheel. *Defiant* is one of a number of Castles which were named after famous Second World War military aircraft.

the spring hangers. Each axle is independently sprung and it is through the adjustment of the springs that the correct axle loadings are achieved for each wheel. This is the process which the locomotive undergoes when the term balancing is used. What happens is that each pair of wheels is weighed and the necessary adjustments made until the weight is properly and evenly distributed, not only for each wheel and axle but for each of the wheels, including bogie and tender wheels.

Incorrectly set weights and improper weight distribution cause not only undue stress and strain, they can also be a factor in a locomotive's propensity to slipping — the more uneven the distribution the more likely the chance of slipping. In severe cases slipping can bring a train to a standstill or prevent it from being started.

In the previous chapters we have covered how steam is raised and how that steam is transmitted to the cylinder to drive the locomotive. We have discussed how steam can be admitted to either side of the piston and how the motion affects this and, in turn, how the pressure of steam on the piston ultimately moves the locomotive. However, this is not quite as straightforward as it may seem. There are two flies in the ointment — one is lost motion and the other is the question of how the engine actually moves.

Does the piston move back inside the cylinder or does the cylinder move forward over the piston? You may want to argue that it is the piston which is moving, but it is the locomotive as a whole which moves forward, or backwards as the case may be. In his book *Locomotive Science Made Easy*, Oliver argues that when the engine is travelling forwards the motion of the piston is continuously forward, with the converse being true when moving backward. Ultimately all that really matters is that motion does occur.

Lost motion is a rather different phenomena and one which must be satisfactorily overcome if the locomotive is not to shake itself to pieces. This term [lost motion] is applied to knocks in the mechanism, and, depending on whether the right or the left crank leads, a knock will develop more quickly in one side driving axlebox and main crankpin than in the opposite.

What happens is that at various times in the

Close-up of the big end of the motion of a rebuilt Bulleid Southern Railway West Country Class Pacific, showing the eccentric rod, crank axle pin, eccentric crank and coupling rod. Note the lubrication 'pots'.

revolution of the driving wheel, thrust is being applied to different parts of either the drive train or the axleboxes. This thrust is taken up by either the crank pin bush, the horn cheek or axlebox wedge.

The correction for lost motion is taken up in the opposite side of the motion or axleboxes to that which is under thrust stress. A single example would be if the thrust is pushing back on the right-hand crank pin. The effect is to try and push the right-hand end of the axle back so forcing the left-hand end of the axle forward, thus increasing the strain on the left front horn cheek and the right rear horn cheek. It is this tendency to try and force the axle back on the thrust side and forward on the free side that must be balanced and controlled.

The construction of the frames takes into account the problem of lost motion. The frames are of rolled steel plate of between one and one and a half inches thickness and are assembled so as to act alternately as a strut and a tie in counteracting the action of the steam pressure against the cylinder.

We have mentioned the horns, but what are they? The horns are triangular section steel castings mounted on the frames on either side of the cut-outs for the axleboxes. They allow the axleboxes to rise or fall within them. The diagram shows their position in relation to the wheel and axlebox and their function, as we have just discussed, is to assist in the control and balancing of the forces which act upon the axles as thrust is applied. The horns are a high stress area and often the horns are further strengthened by the use of a manganese steel liner.

The diagram below also shows how the locomotive is sprung and how the crank axle is built. The huge webs on the axle are to balance out the centrifugal and reciprocating forces created in the reciprocating mass formed of the piston and motion when in motion. It [the web] is a counterweight to balance out those forces.

There are of course a lot of fairly complicated bits of trigonometry and mathematics involved in working out these forces and the weights needed to balance them. What can be said is that a rotational force can be counterbalanced by equal force of rotation in the opposite direction, and that to obtain a balance either the amount or the radius of the [rotational] weight may be altered.

Staying with the frames, they are tied together by cross stays or stretchers, in some cases the inside cylinders, too, and by buffer beams. The frames also carry the bogie and pony or trailing truck mountings, where this is applicable. Additionally there are strengthened cross ties, one of which is known as the drag box, and it is within this section that the intermediate draw gear couplings between the engine and tender are located.

The intermediate draw bar is the coupling between the locomotive and the tender and is thus the shaft through which the motive force at the wheel is transmitted to the pull upon the load. The draw hook is the connection between the locomotive and its train, whichever end the load is attached.

In addition to providing the support platform for the power plant of the locomotive, the boiler and firebox, the frames of the locomotive carry various other important parts mounted on them, including items such as the carrying plates for the springing of the locomotive, the brake gear, running plate, footplate and cab. The frames — and in particular the stretchers — can provide the support for the slide bar assembly in locomotives with inside pistons.

The smokebox is rivetted to the smokebox saddle in which it sits and the saddle is attached between the frames, whilst at the other end the firebox is mounted either across or between the

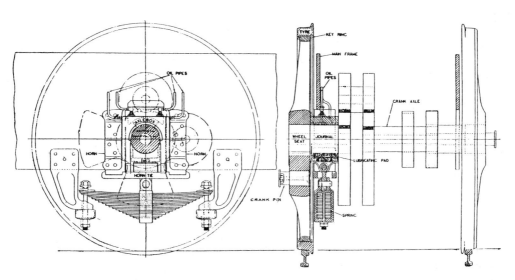

Cross-section and cutaway view of wheel, axlebox, axlebox horns, crank pin, springs, journal, lubricating pad, oil pipes, crank axle and main frame.

frames in such a way as to restrict side-to-side motion but allow expansion in a front to back plane. This is achieved by the use of plates rivetted to the frames and to the outer firebox. Between these plates is an expansion plate with slots rather than holes. This allows the studs to move in one direction but not in the other; this practice was first introduced in the late 1830s by Isaac Dodds, superintendent of the Sheffield and Rotherham Railway, and eventually became more or less standard practice.

We have now covered how the steam is made, how it is transmitted to the wheels and turned into motion at them. We have covered how the wheels are constructed and how they are fitted into the frames which carry the power plant. In other words we have covered the how of making the locomotive move, so it might be advisable at this point to make a few comments on what makes it stop.

The frames carry the support mechanisms of the locomotive braking system, a system which in the majority of cases relies on no more than weight and air pressure to effect the braking effort. There were some locomotives fitted with 'air brakes' in which the braking effort was obtained by forcing the brake blocks against the wheels by using compressed air. However, the vast majority of British locomotive practice relied upon the former rather than the latter method.

The locomotive most often has a steam as well as a vacuum brake and this was particularly the case with freight engines. The brake gear, though, was the same in both cases: metal blocks — brake shoes — were brought into contact with the wheel. *The Engineman's Handbook* describes the process thus: "The function of the brake is to absorb by friction the momentum of the train; in other words, the energy stored in the moving train is converted to heat at the brake blocks when the brakes are applied".

In the early days of railway travel the braking system was very rudimentary, often little more than a hand-operated 'screw-type' brake, using wooden brake blocks. Often the locomotive had brakes only on the driving wheels and some had none at all, the thinking being that the braking stresses transmitted to the axle could cause damage to the axle resulting in their failure. It was not

until the 1860s and 1870s that engine brakes began to be more widespread. Braking was most often carried out by the guard and sometimes he was supported by brakemen. Their brakes were similar to those in use on goods wagons or in guards vans.

However, from 1889 onwards, all passenger trains have been compelled by Act of Parliament to have a continuous braking system, which could be operated either by the driver or the guard and which was self-acting if the train became divided, i.e. it 'failed safe'.

In British locomotive practice the most widely used form of braking has been the steam-operated vacuum brake, though this method is not exclusive and a number of locomotives of various classes and origins have been fitted with air brakes. I will begin with a description of the former and outline the essential differences between the two systems.

In the vacuum brake system the vacuum is created by a device called the 'ejector' — not to be confused with injector. The former ejects air, the latter injects water. Ejectors, like locomotives, come in a variety of shapes and sizes, however, it is the same principle at work whatever the type used. According to *The Engineman's Handbook*, "Steam passing through the steam cone at great velocity is discharged into the ejector air cone where it comes into frictional contact with the air, the steam and air being exhausted through the ejector exhaust pipe and up the chimney via the smokebox elbow". The discharge via the smokebox elbow has no mechanical significance, exhausting via the chimney and smokebox was just convenient.

In the above quote the 'air' is the air in the train pipe. This is either the pipe which runs front to back of the locomotive or its train, if the train consists of vacuum-braked stock. Whilst on the subject of the train pipe it may be pertinent to dispel a popular cinematic cliche — the pulling of the communication cord.

The pulling of the communication cord does not make an emergency application of the brakes. Rather it reduces the vacuum in the train pipe by approximately five to ten inches. This indicates to the driver that the 'cord' has been pulled — he can look back down the train and see

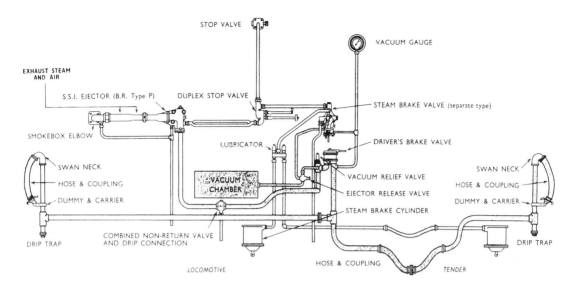

The general arrangement of the vacuum automatic brake on the locomotive and tender. This particular arrangement refers to the British Railways Standard locomotive classes.

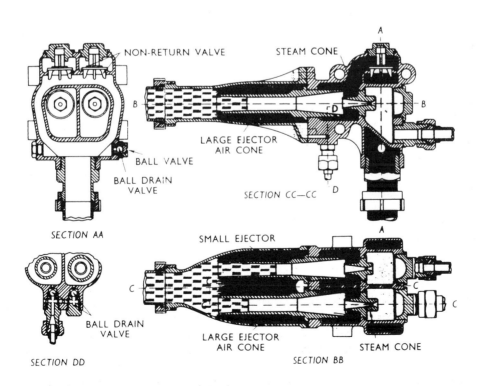

Cross-sections through the large and small ejectors. The ejector is the device through which the vacuum for the continuous braking is created.

by a small metal flag, at the end of each coach, which coach has had the cord pulled. The driver then brings his train to rest clear of any obstructions. He does not stop in a tunnel, nor on a viaduct, either of which might happen if it were the case that the communication cord actually made the emergency application of the brakes one sees in the movies.

Before returning to how the vacuum brake operates, a mention must be made with regard to the existence of both a large and small ejector. The small ejector is for maintaining the vacuum in the train pipe during running while the large

ejector is for creating the initial vacuum and for 'quickly' clearing the brake after an 'in service' application, such as might be made if the distant signal was 'on', but then was 'cleared'. The important difference between the large and small ejector is that the former creates a vacuum much quicker and, being more powerful, will hold a vacuum against a small leakage from the train pipe, such as may occur if the communication cord is pulled.

We can see from the diagram that in addition to the train pipe there is a series of cylinders — these are to be found not only on the locomotive,

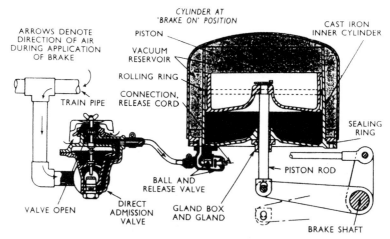

VACUUM BRAKE CYLINDER

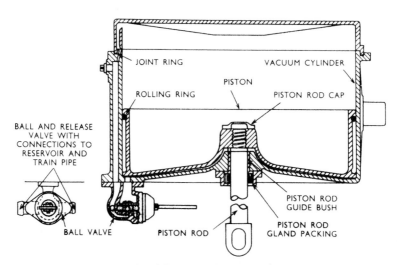

VACUUM BRAKE SEPARATE CYLINDER

The components of the vacuum brake cylinders, and the valves which connect them to the train pipe.

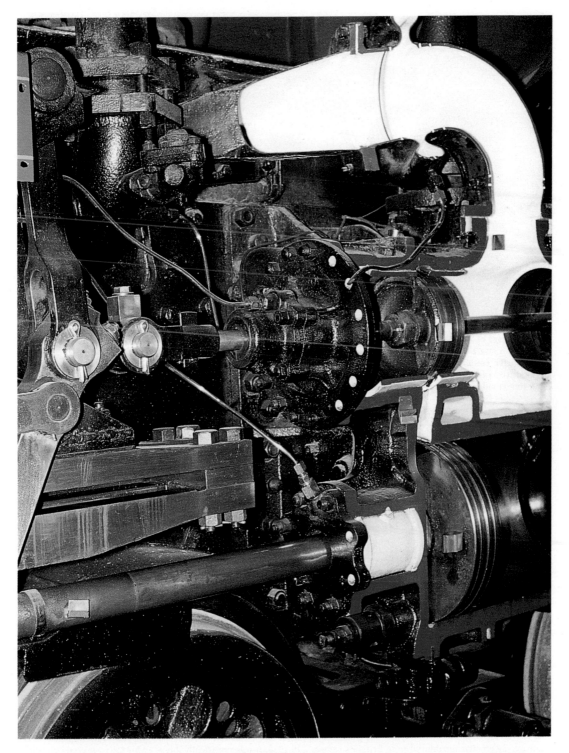

Close-up of the cutaway cylinder of the National Railway Museum's Merchant Navy Class Pacific No 35029 *Ellerman Lines*, an exhibit at the National Railway Museum. Note the steam chest, with the piston valve heads and the piston valve itself. Compare this view with the diagrams of the cylinder function in Chapter Four.

Another usage of the Walschaerts gear, this time as employed on a small-wheeled mixed traffic locomotive, Peppercorn LNER K1 Class 2-6-0 No 2005. Derived from the Gresley K4 Mogul of 1937, this class of seventy locomotives, with 5ft 2in diameter coupled wheels, was introduced in 1949. The survivor, No 2005, is in the care of the North Eastern Locomotive Preservation Group and nominally based on the North Yorkshire Moors Railway, although it is passed for main-line running, too. Note the lubricators mounted on the running plate.

The last of the line: Maunsell's Class V Schools 5P 4-4-0 for the Southern Railway was the last four-coupled express passenger locomotive introduced on to Britain's railways, in 1930. It was specifically intended for the restricted clearances and tight curvature of the Hastings line but worked elsewhere on the Southern system, hauling London−Bournemouth expresses, for example. Note the parallel boiler and round-top firebox. Forty were built, all named after English public schools, and three have survived, including No 30926 *Repton*, based on the North Yorkshire Moors Railway.

The bare bones of a wheelset, in this case the crank axle from Collett Great Western 7800 Manor Class 4-6-0 No 7820 *Dinmore Manor*, currently under restoration at the Birmingham Railway Museum and eventually destined for the West Somerset Railway. Refer to the diagrams in Chapter Six to identify the various components.

The earliest locomotives employed outside frames and large-diameter single driving wheels and these precepts are exemplified in the replica Gooch Iron Duke 2-2-2, which was built in 1985 to commemorate the 150th anniversary of the incorporation of the Great Western Railway. Not evident here is the fact that *Iron Duke* is built to Brunel's seven-foot broad gauge which the GWR defended against the spread of the standard gauge until 1892.

The archetypal British locomotive, at least until the turn of the century, has to be the six-coupled goods engine. Every major company, with the exception of the Great Western, continued to build 0-6-0s in quantity right up to the 1930s. Among them, was the North Eastern Railway which had a huge traffic in coal and minerals throughout Durham and Northumberland. Wilson Worsdell's Class P3 (LNER Class J27) 5F 0-6-0 was introduced in 1906 and construction continued up to 1923, with the now-preserved No 2392 becoming the last locomotive built for the NER at Darlington. Here, No 2392 displays its large boiler, 4ft 7½in diameter wheels and inside Stephenson gear.

One of the classic examples of a compound locomotive, the de Glehn/du Bosquet 4-6-0 built for the Nord Railway of France. The locomotive is fitted with two regulators, the low pressure valve to assist starting and the main regulator to put the locomotive into full compound working. It employs the Lemaître multiple-jet blastpipe and a Duplex reverser to give independent cut-off to high and low pressure valve gears. Curiously, this historic French locomotive is part of the British national collection and currently kept — out of traffic — on the Nene Valley Railway.

Patrick Stirling's famous single-wheeler for the Great Northern Railway, built at Doncaster in 1870 and employing — at eight feet — the largest diameter driving wheel ever employed on a British locomotive design. The theory was elegantly simple: the larger the wheel diameter, the greater the distance covered in a single revolution. Unfortunately, increasing trainloads with their greater demands on adhesion (which comes from smaller wheels and more of them) spelled the demise of the single-wheeler. GNR No 1 is part of the national collection and on display in the National Railway Museum, York.

At the other extreme of Victorian locomotive design comes the typical six-coupled industrial saddletank. This example, *Lindsay*, was built by the Wigan Coal and Iron Company of Lancashire to work its own colliery railway system. It employs the Ramsbottom-type safety valves which were later supplanted by the Ross 'pop' type, and displays the large dome typical of a saturated (*ie* non-superheated) locomotive. This veteran can be found not far from its original home, at Steamtown Railway Museum, Carnforth.

Cab interior of Riddles BR Standard Class 8P Pacific No 71000 *Duke of Gloucester*. When designing the cabs for the Standard classes, Robert Riddles made the point of asking footplate crews to comment on the proposed layout and produced a mock-up to enable them to do this. However, though ergonomically sound, in practice some of the cabs proved uncomfortably draughty. Refer to the diagram on page 73 to identify the principal cab controls.

Showing his usual independence of thought, the Southern Railway's Oliver Bulleid decided to move away from the conventional spoked wheel for his Pacific designs (and for the later Q1 class 0-6-0) and developed a lighter yet stronger alternative in collaboration with steelmakers, Firth-Brown. The BFB wheel, as it was patented, is seen here on West Country Class Pacific No 34023 *Blackmore Vale*, currently under overhaul on the Bluebell Railway.

Cab interior of a Swindon-built locomotive, showing the right-hand drive employed on all Great Western locomotives. Prominent are the red regulator handle (centre) and the red reversing gear handle on the right. To the left of that can be seen the hydrostatic lubricator and, to the left of the regulator, the water level gauge. To the left of that sit the steam heating pressure gauge (lower) and the boiler pressure gauge (upper). Above the lubricator, is the blower valve, the ejector steam valve and the brake handle, with the vacuum brake gauge above that. This particular cab belongs to Collett 2251 Class 3MT 0-6-0 No 3205, currently operating on the West Somerset Railway.

but also on all other items of vacuum braked rolling stock, be they coaches or wagons. It is through the operating of these cylinders that brake applications are effected.

As may be seen from the diagram, the cylinder houses a piston and is connected to the train pipe via a ball valve and flexible hose. The system can be seen to consist of a vacuum reservoir and cylinder combined, the cylinder being open at the top and enclosed within the reservoir. The brake piston is an airtight fit within the cylinder and the piston rod passes through an airtight gland in the base of the cylinder.

The purpose of the 'ball valve' is to control the movement of the brake piston in accordance with the variations in the train pipe vacuum, and also to provide a means of releasing the brake by hand when necessary. This is the valve which is affected when train crew refer to 'pulling the strings' — a task which would have to be done whenever a former GWR engine was being replaced as train engine by a locomotive from one of the other railways, which would draw only twenty-one inches of vacuum as opposed to the twenty-five of the GWR. The Great Western also employed, in addition to the ejector, a vacuum pump, which was driven via one of the piston crossheads. As far as I am able to ascertain the vacuum pump, which was only operational during motion, was used to reduce the amount of steam used in the operation of the large ejector, when effecting a quick release of the brake.

When the locomotive and/or its train is running with the brake off, the 'ball valve' is unseated, leaving the train pipe in communication with both sides of the piston, which will then be in equilibrium, and resting by its own weight at the bottom of the cylinder. Immediately air is admitted to the train pipe, either by the driver or guard making an application of the brake or by a break in the train pipe. It [the air] passes up the connecting pipe and forces the ball valve to its seating on the port leading to the vacuum chamber, thereby retaining the vacuum on the topside of the piston. The port to the underside of the piston is left open, by the movement of the ball, and the air then flows into the bottom of the cylinder, lifts the piston and hence applies the brakes.

This is, in essence, how the vacuum brake operates: the operation of the steam brake and the air brake are slightly different. In the case of the air brake, compressed air is used to force the brake shoe against the wheel. This allows the use of smaller pistons than those used in the vacuum brake system, as the air used to operate the pistons is at several times atmospheric pressure.

In the steam brake it is steam pressure which acts upon the brake piston, which forces the brake shoe against the wheel. However, unlike the air and vacuum brake systems, the steam brake is operational on the engine and tender only and not upon the rest of the train, irrespective of what type of rolling stock the train consists of.

In locomotives with a combined steam/vacuum brake (probably the most common system in British locomotive practice), the operation of the vacuum brake actuates the steam brake. When air is admitted to the train pipe and the vacuum cylinder piston begins to rise it effects the closure of the steam brake cylinder exhaust valve. As it continues to move up it opens the steam valve to the steam brake cylinder. However, whatever system is used the effect is the same. The steam brake on the locomotive operates fractionally later than the train brake (though when running light engine this is obviously not the case).

On locomotives designed to work with air braked rolling stock a steam driven compressor would be used. Several railways used air braked stock and locomotives: the Great Eastern, London Brighton and South Coast, Caledonian and North British were just some of the companies to adopt this system in whole or in part. Several classes of heavy freight locomotive types, most notably the Riddles Austerities and his 9F 2-10-0s, were fitted with air braking systems often in addition to the more commonly used vacuum ejector arrangement.

The air brake was developed by the American engineer George Westinghouse, though the actual specification for the system was British in origin. The name of Westinghouse is almost synonymous with brake systems and also has a high profile within the signal and telegraph side of railway operation. However, in the days of steam the use of air brake systems was the exception rather than the rule it has become with more modern forms of railway locomotion.

Today the steam-operated Westinghouse-type air brake system is employed on a number of narrow gauge lines, the most recent converts to this type of system being the Talyllyn and the Vale of Rheidol.

Related to the braking system, whether it be of the air or vacuum variety, is the ATC or AWS (Automatic Train Control or the Automatic Warning System). The former was developed in the early years of the twentieth century by the Great Western Railway, whilst the latter was adopted as a standard system following nationalisation.

While the two systems are slightly different in operation, the aim is the same: improved safety for the travelling public and to a lesser extent minimising of delays during periods of poor visibility. The AWS system was essentially developed from the GWR's ATC.

The AWS is operated by a system of magnets both in the tracks and attached to the locomotive. The track-based magnets are of two types, one a fixed magnet, the other an electro magnet. If the signal is at caution the electro magnet is 'dead' — if this is the case a hooter sounds in the cab and a visual indication is given on the AWS box, the 'driver's control unit'. The driver must acknowledge this warning by depressing the reset handle on the AWS box. If the driver fails to acknowledge the warning then a brake application is made automatically. If the signal is at clear a bell sounds and no action need be taken.

On the locomotive, and its tender if it is a tender engine, the brakes themselves are attached to hangers and an arrangement which provides for the adjustment of the brakes. In addition to acting as the carrier for the brake gear, the frame also supports the running plate and in the early years of the steam locomotive the running plate was an important part of the locomotive. It allowed the driver to move from the footplate around the locomotive, whilst in motion, to add oil, and to make visual examinations that all was in order with important moving parts, bearings etc. However, as refinements and improvements

were effected the running plate, for these purposes, became redundant and so access to them from the footplate ceased.

The running plate, though less important than it once was, has other uses. Frequently it is used as the mounting point for the mechanical lubricator, it provides access to the sand boxes, and to the oiling points on the inside motion of locomotives with inside cylinders. The running plates also provide a work platform for fitters working on items such as the clacks or upper boiler fittings, like the dome or safety valves.

Another of the items attached to the frames and in part accessed from the running plate are the sanders. These may be steam operated or gravity fed. Both types perform the same task though in the case of the former the sand is blown under the wheel by a jet of steam. The sanders are used to help increase adhesion between the steel wheel and steel rail in wet or icy conditions when adhesion is lessened and slipping results. The idea is that sand blown under the wheels helps to improve the grip, but while the system may work well enough in theory, the practice is something of a hit and miss affair.

The cab, the one place all small, and not so small, boys want to be, is more correctly referred to as the footplate — it is the area in which the crew work and the major controls of the locomotive are situated. In the early days of locomotion, when it was 'wooden engines and iron men', there were no cabs, or to be more precise there were no roofs: indeed almost no protection from the elements at all. The cab like the locomotives themselves 'developed'. Similarly as the locomotives developed so too did the fixtures and fittings incorporated into the footplate area.

Two of the major items of equipment within the footplate area are the control for making the engine go forwards or backwards — the reversing lever — and the means to open or close the supply of steam to the cylinders — the regulator. In operational conditions these two controls are operated in conjunction. The degree to which the reversing lever is set determines the length of time steam is admitted to the cylinder. The amount by which the regulator is open determines the pressure and volume of steam

Cab of Collett GWR King Class 8P 4-6-0 No 6024 *King Edward I*. Displaying its usual independence, the Great Western differed from most other British railway companies in adopting right-hand drive for its locomotives.

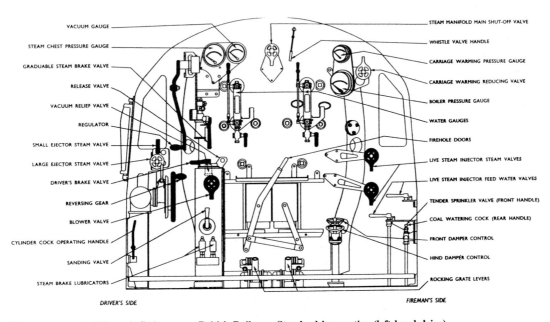

The arrangement of the cab fittings on a British Railways Standard locomotive (left-hand drive).

admitted during the opening of the admission port in the cylinder.

What can be made to go must also be capable of being stopped, so in addition to the reversing lever and the regulator there is also a brake, indeed as we have already stated there are steam brakes, vacuum brakes, air brakes and hand brakes, but whatever the type, the operation is from a handle on the footplate. Some locomotives have separate steam and vacuum brakes, others have these combined into one. All have a hand brake, and as I've already mentioned it is also the case that in the very early days of steam traction the hand brake was the only brake.

We've dealt with the controls which stop, start or reverse the direction of travel, but these are only a part of the footplate apparatus. In the top of the cab and attached to the boiler back plate is the main steam manifold. This manifold controls the supply of steam to such items as the steam brake, the ejector, the injectors, the train heating system, and where applicable, to the system of atomised lubrication — the sight-feed lubricator. There will also be shut off valves for items such as the whistle, steam sanders and steam generator, where fitted; likewise such items as coal pushers, steam reversers and sand guns.

Below the manifold, but still on the back plate, are the gauge glasses. The gauge glasses indicate the level of water above the firebox crown plate which must at all times, when the engine is in steam, be covered by water. Failure to keep the crown plate covered with water can have catastrophic consequences, not only for the firebox but also for the footplate crew who could be burnt or scalded if the crown plate were to become uncovered.

If the crown plate became uncovered the fusible plugs in the crown plate would blow as a first event or in an extreme case the crown plate could collapse. This would fill the firebox with steam at boiler pressure. If the firebox door happened to be open at the time, flames, coals, searing hot gases and steam could enter the confined area of the cab with obvious consequences for those present.

Other items of cab equipment are steam pressure gauges for; boiler pressure, train heating pipe pressure and on some locomotives steam chest pressure. There are vacuum gauges which show the number of inches of vacuum being maintained in the train pipe and in the reservoir. There are levers or steam valves which activate things like the steam sanders, blower, cylinder drain cocks, steam and water supplies to the injectors and steam and oil supplies to the sight-feed lubricator.

The level of equipment on the footplate varies from locomotive to locomotive and some of the items not yet mentioned include the actuating mechanism for the drop or rocker grate, the slacker pipe, the whistle, the scoop, the lighting generator, the damper controls, oil-feed boxes, blow down valves, tender or tank water level gauges and — on Bulleid Pacifics — steam-operated firehole doors. The unrebuilt Bulleid Pacifics also had steam operated reversers as did the Q1 Austerities, though it must be said that Bulleid was not the only designer to incorporate the steam-operated reverser.

When the locomotive was readied for traffic, numerous other items would be found in the footplate area: a tin of detonators and red flag, an assortment of spanners, a coal pick, firing shovel, bucket, hand brush, fire irons, bottles of oil, paraffin, spare gauge glasses, gauge glass lamp, head/tail lamps, brake stick and in some cases a tarpaulin sheet for use when running tender first in bad weather.

Standing on the footplate with one's back to the backplate you would see on the left the handle for applying the hand brake and on the right a handle for operating the 'scoop'. The scoop was an essential element in being able to run long distances non-stop. Were it not for the scoop the average 5,000 gallons would be all used in around one hundred or so miles — a long way short of Glasgow or Edinburgh. The scoop made it possible to collect water from troughs placed between the tracks. It was fine in theory but also tricky to avoid spraying water in all directions by not getting the scoop out of the trough quickly enough once the tender was full.

The tender, in addition to being the water carrier, also has the coal space. This is often shaped in such a way as to encourage the coal to roll toward the shovelling plate at the footplate end of the tender. The tender is generally the

Footplate of a rebuilt Bulleid Southern Railway Merchant Navy Class Pacific. Note the Ajax patent firedoors.

This angle on Riddles Standard Class 4MT 2-6-0 No 76079 shows the detail of its six-wheel tender. Note the inset coal bunker, and the spectacle glass of the tender cab, designed to aid visibility during tender-first running.

location of the space to store the necessary fire irons: the 'paddle', a long-handled metal shovel; the 'pricker', a kind of single toothed rake; and the 'dart' a sort of poker for lifting the fire. The tender was also the home for the driver's and fireman's locker and the tool locker for spanners, spare gauge glasses, detonators and the like.

There were one or two classes of locomotive with some rather unique features incorporated into the tender. Some of the Coronation Class Pacifics on the LMS had steam-operated coal pushers. This device was needed because on the long non-stop runs from London to Glasgow much of the tender's coal supply would be used. Without a pusher, the fireman would be walking backwards and forwards to get each shovelful, or

having to work in the tender, pulling coal down to the shovelling plate whilst the engine was in motion — something you just don't do.

The LNER built tenders with a passageway or corridor between the footplate and the leading coach. This allowed for crew changes on their long non-stop runs. Some tenders have been built with sprinkler systems incorporated so that the coal could be kept damped and thus reduce the level of swirling coal dust on the footplate.

The tender was in general of six or eight wheel construction with the inevitable exceptions being a number which were of bogie construction. The size of a tender and its coal and water capacity would be dependent on the type of locomotive it was designed to be coupled to and the nature of the work it would perform. Consideration would also be given to the area of the system on which it would work and thus engines of a single class or type might be fitted with any one of several differently sized tenders depending on its particular allocation and application.

The tank engine does not, as you will have guessed, have a tender and its coal is carried in the bunker and its water in the side tanks. The tanks themselves can be of a number of different styles: they may be side, saddle or pannier. The latter were almost the trademark of the GWR and as their name suggests they were hung from the sides of boiler. The saddle tank on the other hand is draped over the boiler — like the saddle on a horse and the side tank is just that — on the side of the boiler but separate from it.

The tanks are interconnected by a pipe, known as the equalisation pipe which keeps the water level in each tank identical. Often tank engines were built as a variant of the tender locomotive with the only difference being that the tank engine had a lengthened main frame to incorporate the bunker, but was in all other major respects identical to its tendered sister.

This brings us to the end of our description of the essential features of locomotives and how they work. However, no description of how the steam locomotive works would be complete with a chapter on how the crew make the locomotive carry out its allotted duties and how their performances determine the locomotive's performance.

CHAPTER 7

Men of the Footplate – How They Work

The task of making the locomotive work and keeping it working is carried out on the footplate. To bring a locomotive into steam takes hours rather than minutes and with a large locomotive five or even six hours might be needed to raise sufficient steam to move the engine. However, once steam has been raised keeping it there is, as any fireman will tell you, not quite as easy as you may think.

If you recall, at the outset of this book I remarked that in order to make a locomotive work it is required that the crew work together as a team, and that how well they did so in part determined the capability of the locomotive. It will help to understand how the locomotive works if in addition to all that has been said already, you have some appreciation of how the team of driver and fireman perform this task.

Different types of train and different classes of locomotive require different driving and firing methods. One wouldn't fire the tank engine on station pilot in the same manner as firing the 'Mid-Day Scot', similarly one wouldn't drive the 'Atlantic Coast Express' in the same style as the pick-up freight or indeed any loose-coupled train.

Before leaving shed to commence a 'turn of duty' the locomotive would be 'prepared', i.e. a whole series of tasks would be undertaken by both driver and fireman. After booking on, a crew would check the locomotive roster board to discover which locomotive they would use and whereabouts in the shed the locomotive was standing.

Once on the footplate the following tasks would begin: the fireman would check the level of water in the boiler and spread the fire; the driver would get out the oil and oil can. If the weather was cold he would put the oil to warm either up on the manifold or on the warming plate above the firehole door. Having spread the fire and added some fresh coals the fireman would check that the engine had all its necessary equipment, fire irons, coal pick, gauge lamp, engine lamps, detonators, red flag, oil, paraffin, spare gauge glasses and seals, spanners, bucket, hand brush and tender sheet, if such an item was needed. The driver would be oiling round and examining the locomotive and would send the fireman to the stores to make good any deficiency in the engine's equipment or to draw whatever oils were needed.

The fireman would be slowly building up his fire and then doing jobs such as sweeping the framing and running plate clear of any smokebox ash, checking that the smokebox door was securely fastened. Before leaving shed he would also check the coal and water levels, topping up as needed, the injectors would be used so as to ensure they were working properly. The coal would be 'trimmed', that is it would be made safe against any lumps falling from the tender which could injure platelayers, gangers or passengers. These tasks would take the crew about an hour to complete and the fireman's final job before leaving the shed would be to brew the tea — arguably the most important of his footplate duties.

The checks the driver would make included testing the vacuum and steam brakes, examining the flexible hoses for the vacuum brake and for the train heating. He would also be looking for

Waiting for the green. One of the crew of Stanier LMS Class 5MT 4-6-0 No 5407 awaits the road at York, ready to back down to the station to take out a railtour to Scarborough in August 1981.

any signs of excess wear in such items as the brake blocks, bearings and tyres and he would check for excessive side play in the rods and take overall responsibility for all the tasks undertaken in preparing the engine to work its train.

To move the engine 'off shed' the hand brake would be released and the reversing lever moved into fore or back gear depending on which way the locomotive was to proceed, then with the cylinder cocks open the regulator would be opened to set the engine in motion. The movement of the locomotive would increase the draught on the fire and the fireman, depending on the nature of the day's duty, would continue to build up the fire.

The firing of the locomotive in traffic is determined by the extent to which the regulator is opened and the degree of cut-off on the reversing lever. The distance to travel and the gradients to be encountered also have an effect on the firing. However, these are not the only items; different locomotives and different classes of locomotive respond differently to the level and shape of the fire.

There are one or two rules of thumb inasmuch as most locomotive types tend to steam if the back corners and the area just under the firehold are kept well banked up. However, there are some locomotives which will 'go sick' if the fire exceeds five to seven inches over any part of the grate. Equally there are some locomotives which steam so well that they could be worked with a fire over a foot thick. In general a fire which was thicker at the back and tapered towards the front of the gate was the ideal. With some engines, getting the fire too thick at the front of the grate would result in shortages of steam. Knowing the engine, the road and the driver was always a help in firing.

Driving a locomotive involved not only opening

Performing the vital task of oiling round on Collett GWR Castle Class 7P 4-6-0 No 5080 *Defiant*. Attention here is being given to the crosshead and slidebars as *Defiant* waits to take out the last Shakespeare Express shuttle of the day between Stratford-upon-Avon and Tyseley (Birmingham) on April 16, 1990.

Ready to roll. The driver of Stanier LMS 8F 2-8-0 No 48151 exchanges a word with a fellow footplateman as the big freight engine comes off shed at Carnforth, a scene redolent of the Fifties and Sixties. But this was Steamtown Railway Museum in March 1991 and No 48151 — wearing a Normanton (55E) shedplate — was rostered to do nothing more strenuous than work Steamtown's Crag Bank shuttle. However, the 8F has made a number of appearances on the main line in recent years.

and closing the regulator and altering the degree of cut-off, it also required the driver to 'know the road'. This meant that he would know the gradients, the position of signals and the routes to which they applied — this was essential knowledge when approaching junctions, especially at night. Before ever a driver was put in charge of a train he had to have route knowledge and often several weeks were spent just riding along a particular route with a suitably qualified driver, learning all the signals gradients and idiosyncrasies of that particular route.

Driving a locomotive hauling a loose-coupled goods train is a very different task to that employed in driving a passenger or vacuum-fitted train. In a loose-coupled train the train has to be 'eased out', this means that the locomotive must be moved slowly and carefully until all the

couplings have been drawn out taut. Only when this has been done can the regulator be opened up to get the train underway. It's a bit like towing one car with another using a length of rope, one can only get going once the rope is drawn tight. When bringing a goods train to a stand each of the couplings has to be 'drawn in', the braking must be gentle until all the wagons have been allowed to buffer up. Failure to follow these procedures can result in a broken coupling, or, worse, a derailment.

With loose-coupled trains the changes in gradient of the track can also affect the way the locomotive is driven. In the case of severe down gradients it may even be necessary to stop the train and pin down brakes on the wagons, using the brake stick. Those of you who know the Keighley and Worth Valley line may have noticed a sign at Oxenhope telling the crew to stop and pin down brakes before proceeding. These were once a commonplace, though with the advent of fully-fitted stock they are now superfluous.

The driver would not only have to have route knowledge but also a great deal of knowledge about the locomotive itself and the company's rules and regulations. He would need details of all engineering work on the route being taken so each week drivers were issued with a booklet containing all such works being carried out on the routes over which they would work. The notices gave all the details of where and how severe speed restrictions were, or where signal boxes would be closed or where pilotmen would be available in the case of temporary diversion. Whilst it is true that this information tells you nothing about how the locomotive works it does tell you something about how the crew are trained and how they manage their often thankless tasks.

Hopefully it will give you a better insight into the skills and duties of the men who made rail travel one of, if not the safest modes of transport.

Alas the national network of railways is now a shadow of its former self and the steam locomotive once such a common sight is now an anachronistic relic of an age long gone. Pampered and cosseted, the few remaining examples spend their days chuffing up and down a few miles of former branch line — a duty few of them were actually built for. However, there are a few locomotives which still do what they were designed to do — these are the locomotives which haul the special steam services run over the lines of the national network.

In the concluding chapter we look at just what the steam locomotive has to undergo in order to work over the railway it was designed to run on. The tests and examinations which make up the railway locomotive equivalent of the MOT certificate — MT276.

CHAPTER 8

Exams and Inspections

Nowadays the steam locomotive is confined to the preserved railways and a few specially selected routes on the national network. However, despite their disappearance as the motive power for our railway services, the preserved locomotive must still be maintained to the highest standards and there is a special department at British Rail Derby and a number of senior traction inspectors who are specially concerned with the examination of locomotives being used on the BR lines. Equally there are specialist examiners from the insurance companies who ensure that the steam engines which run on today's railways are safe to do so.

The major examination today is known as MT 276 and this is what takes place when this two-part exam is carried out. Two men attached to Derby Work's technical staff, who are, respectively British Rail's chief boiler examiner and chief mechanical inspector, will visit the locomotive on site and carry out a whole battery of tests and examinations before prescribing the engine fit for duty.

Unlike many visits by officials, the visits of BR's technical examiners are not viewed with trepidation, or if they are the fitters and boilersmiths do a remarkable job of hiding it. What comes over is the respect that all parties have for each other's knowledge and abilities, and the free flow of ideas and information which takes place is a credit to all concerned. However, from the thoroughness of the exam of the locomotive it is equally apparent that this camaraderie does not prevent the proper execution of responsibility — 'if it wasn't right then it would have to be put right or there would be no main-line turn'.

The first examination, referred to as the 'cold exam' is, as the name suggests, an examination of the locomotive out of steam. The boiler is drained of water and the washout plugs and mudhole doors are all removed to allow a thorough examination of the stays and water space — a task which is aided by the use of mirrors.

The current mode of dress for a boiler exam is hooded fluorescent orange overalls, which the examiner dons before entering the firebox to begin the first of his checks. In the firebox the tube ends and tubeplate are examined — the tube ends for signs of leakage or any wasting of the beaded ends, the tubeplate for scoring and cracks. Next an examination of the brick arch and the fusible plugs before going onto what must be one of, if not the, noisiest examination.

To check the soundness of the stays they are literally sounded. In a manner not unlike that of the legendary 'wheel tapper', the boiler examiner goes round inside the firebox hammering the rivetted ends of the stays and listening to the sounds they make — any difference in the tone indicates cracked or broken stays. Whilst this racket is taking place in the firebox the mechanical inspector is methodically plodding round the engine and tender wheels checking the flange and tyre tread wear.

On paper it all sounds so quick and easy, but when you consider that there are hundreds of stays in the firebox and that a specially constructed gauge has to be properly located and two sets of measurements taken from each set of wheels then you begin to get some idea of how time-consuming the exam becomes.

When the examination of the tyre thickness,

security and profile has been completed, the inspection moves on to checking for excess play in the motion, or for fractured or broken springs. This latter involves crawling around underneath the locomotive, between the frames. If the engine has inside motion this will also be checked along with items such as horns, axles and the frames themselves for any signs of cracks or wear. The attention to detail is remarkable. Are all the split pins in place? Are there any signs of slippage between wheel and tyre? Are the guard irons secure? What is the condition of the draw hook and the screw coupling? Not even the whistle wire goes unchecked.

After completing an internal inspection of the stays and firebox the next task of the boiler examiner is to inspect the water and steam space between the inner and outer plates of the firebox. Armed with a lighted taper and an item which looks as though it may have fallen off a recent space shuttle, but which is actually a mirror mounted in such a way as to allow it to be adjusted through several angles in the confined space between the inner and out firebox plates, the inspector is able to check the stays for wasting or fracture, a visual as opposed to audible check, and to examine the firebox plates for scouring or cracks.

The second of the two examinations, the 'in steam' examination, usually takes place a week to ten days after the cold exam and in this exam the items under scrutiny are the operations of the injectors and ejector, the water gauge, steam gauge, superheater elements, safety valves, brakes, and a further examination of the firebox — though not by crawling about inside. This time the inspection is made from the footplate using a mirror on the firing shovel to see the inaccessible bits on the backplate or upper rear corners of the crown plate.

The ejector is tested by removing the flexible brake hose from its dumb connection on the locomotive and covering the end of the pipe with a blanking plate drilled with a small hole — the ejector must be able to maintain the vacuum against the leakage caused by the hole. The test for the superheater elements and header consists of pressurising this system by opening the regulator with the brakes on and the cylinder

cocks closed, thus allowing steam to pass from the regulator valve through the main internal steam pipe and thence through the superheater tubes and the superheater header to the steam chest.

The visual examination of the superheater is made from the smokebox and when this test is complete the smokebox tubeplate is examined for leaks, the blower ring checked and the smokebox door fastenings examined. The examination of the safety valves is done during the in steam exam and this check is done not against the locomotive's own steam pressure gauge, but against a standard gauge. First the top nut from one of the gauge glasses is removed and in its place goes the standard gauge — the steam riser then brings the locomotive up to blowing off point and the point at which the safety valves lift and re-seat is measured against the standard gauge.

The examination of a leading preserved railway's boilershop black museum would show just the sort of things these examinations are designed to detect, stays wasted to the thickness of a fountain pen, scored, pitted firebox and boiler plates, less than half their original thickness. We might moan about the cost, or the failure of our favourite locomotive, but there is no doubt that the work of British Rail's technical inspection department does make life much safer for us all.

We have now covered most of the major components in the construction and workings of the steam locomotive. There are of course many variations which have been glossed over or mentioned in name only. In a contraption which evolved over a period spanning more than one hundred and fifty years, this is to be expected. However, it is hoped that this and the preceding chapters have given you a basic understanding of how the steam locomotive fulfils its duty.

During the writing of this book a number of terms and jargon words have had to be used — though hopefully they have been explained sufficiently to allow a rough and ready understanding of them. To assist in the reading of, or reference to these words, terms, or jargon it is hoped that the glossary which follows this chapter will be of some assistance.

Glossary

Ash pans located below the fire grate the ash pans are part of the system which controls the flow of air to the fire. Flaps attached to the ash pans (the dampers), control the admission of primary air.

Baffle plate a half round plate which fits into the firehole and directs the secondary air supply below the nose of the brick arch and towards the firebed.

Blast pipe the pipe carrying exhaust steam from the cylinders out to the atmosphere.

Blower a ring of steam jets located round the blast pipe orifice. The blower is used to create a partial vacuum in the smokebox, when coasting or when steam raising with the locomotive static.

Brick arch a construction of fire bricks in the firebox, which ensures that the combustible gases given off by the coal are properly burned. It also helps to retain heat in the firebox, reducing stresses and strains caused by heating and cooling.

Clacks a non-return valve usually located on the upper part of the boiler. It allows water from the injector to enter the boiler but prevents steam escaping from it.

Combustion chamber an extension of the firebox into the boiler barrel it increases the heating surface.

Crosshead is the point of connection between the piston and the connecting rod. In addition to being the connection between piston and connecting rod the crosshead, in conjunction with the slide bars, also guides the piston rod and absorbs any oblique thrust delivered by the connecting rod.

Crown plate the plate which is the roof of the firebox, it contains the fusible plugs and must at all times be kept covered by water.

Dampers hinged flaps fitted to the ash pans these flaps control the flow of primary air to the underside of the fire.

Drag box a specially strengthened cross member, it is located at the rear of the main frame and is the point of attachment for the intermediate draw gear between engine and tender.

Eccentric a device which translates rotary motion into reciprocating movement to actuate the valves. In the Stephenson-type motion two eccentrics are used, one to make the locomotive move forward, the other to reverse.

Ejector a device which uses high velocity steam passing through a series of cones to create a vacuum in the train pipe. It is the means by which the vacuum for the continuous brake is created.

Expansion the term used to denote the part of the piston stroke which is effected after the closing of the admission port and before the opening of the exhaust port.

Fusible plug often referred to simply as the plug, this is a safety device designed to protect the firebox in the event of a shortage of water. Located in the firebox crown plate the plug has a lead core which if it is not covered by water melts. If the core does melt it allows steam at boiler pressure to enter the firebox — this puts out the fire.

Horns triangular pieces of steel plate attached to the frames at the point where the axle cut-outs occur. The horns are part of the means for ensuring the control of lost motion and the stability of the axle in the frame.

'Hydraulicing' railwaymen's slang for what happens if water is drawn into the cylinders via the regulator valve which is then prevented from closure by the presence of the water.

Injector a device for putting water into the boiler against the pressure of steam in the boiler.

Jimmy railwaymen's slang for a device which was fitted across the blast pipe orifice in locomotives which were steam shy. The device itself is simply a metal cross and its effect was to sharpen the blast by restricting the blast pipe orifice.

Journal the section of axle immediately behind the wheel, which is buffed and polished to form a bearing surface for the fitting of the axlebox.

Lap and lead lap is the amount by which the valve heads overlap the steam port with the reversing lever in mid-gear. Lead is the amount by which the valve is open to steam at the end of the piston stroke.

Manifold a large casting which collects steam from the boiler on the inlet side and distributes it through a series of manually operable cut-off valves to such items of equipment as the injectors, ejector, train heating system, blower and the like.

Motion a blanket term used to cover all the rods, links and levers which make up the locomotive drive train.

Mud hole any one of a number of openings in the outer firebox plates which gives access to the water space between the two sets of plates (see also **Washout**).

Pendulum link also known as the combination lever, this is the link between the valve gear and the crosshead, via the union link, in the Walschaerts motion.

Pony truck an independently sprung and mounted small diameter wheel fitted behind the rear driving wheel on some locomotives. The pony truck is a more sophisticated version of a radial axle first introduced by F. W. Webb.

Primary air air which is drawn through the firebed, the amount and direction of which is controlled by the dampers.

Priming is the term which is given to water being picked up and carried through into the cylinders. If priming occurs at high speed it can result in serious damage to the cylinders or the motion.

Radius rod in Walschaerts motion this is the rod which connects the valve spindle to the reversing lever, though this is not a direct connection. The radius rod effects the change in the length of time the valves are open to admit steam to the cylinder.

Sand gun a steam-powered sand blaster which is used to clear soot and char from the smoke and flue tubes.

Saturated steam steam even at high pressures still contains small droplets of water, i.e. it is wet or saturated. Until the early years of the twentieth century all locomotives were saturated steam engines. However, from about 1910/11 onwards the majority of locomotives and especially the larger express engines were superheated.

Scaling impurities in the water cause a build-up of solids in the water space, the solids are referred to as scale and hence the term.

Scoop a device operated by the fireman which allows water to be collected from troughs set between the rails. This arrangement made possible the long non-stop runs such as those from London to Carlisle or Edinburgh. The only railway not to use troughs was the Southern.

Scouring the name used to denote what happens when loose scale is percolated round the water space by the boiling water. The pieces of scale score and damage the firebox plates.

Sight-feed lubricator a cab-mounted device, which could be controlled and adjusted by the footplate crew, to supply atomised oil to the cylinders.

Slacker pipe also known as the 'pet pipe', 'fizzle pipe' and probably other colloquial terms. This was a supply of hot water which would be used to dampen the coal in the tender and to keep the footplate area damp. This helped to prevent coal dust blowing about and getting in the crew's eyes.

Snifting valve also known as the anti-vacuum valve, these valves are fitted to locomotives with superheaters and allow air to be drawn into the cylinders when running with the regulator closed — 'coasting'.

Superheating a process by which saturated steam is passed through a series of tubes, housed in the large flue tubes, and in being treated in this way is dried i.e. the water droplets of the saturated steam are also turned to steam. This method of drying the steam increases its volume and in so doing improves its efficiency. Tests showed savings in coal consumption of up to 25 percent with the use of superheating.

Stays threaded metal rods used to hold the inner and outer sections of the firebox together or to hold the firebox to the boiler barrel.

'Taps' railwayman's term for the cylinder drain cocks.

Thermic syphon a device used in some locomotives to increase the heating area and to improve the circulation of the boiler water.

Washout every so many miles or days the locomotive would be drained of water and the water spaces would be swilled out, removing all the built-up deposits of scale, which if left, would reduce steaming efficiency and reduce the life of the boiler.

Webs the large weights used to counterbalance the reciprocating mass formed of, or by, the motion when in motion.